THE HOLLYWOOD QUIZ BOOK

THE HOLLYWOOD QUIZ BOOK

Eric Saunders

This edition published in 2009 by Arcturus Publishing Limited
26/27 Bickels Yard, 151–153 Bermondsey Street,
London SE1 3HA

ISBN: 978-1-84837-223-8
AD000254EN

Printed in Singapore

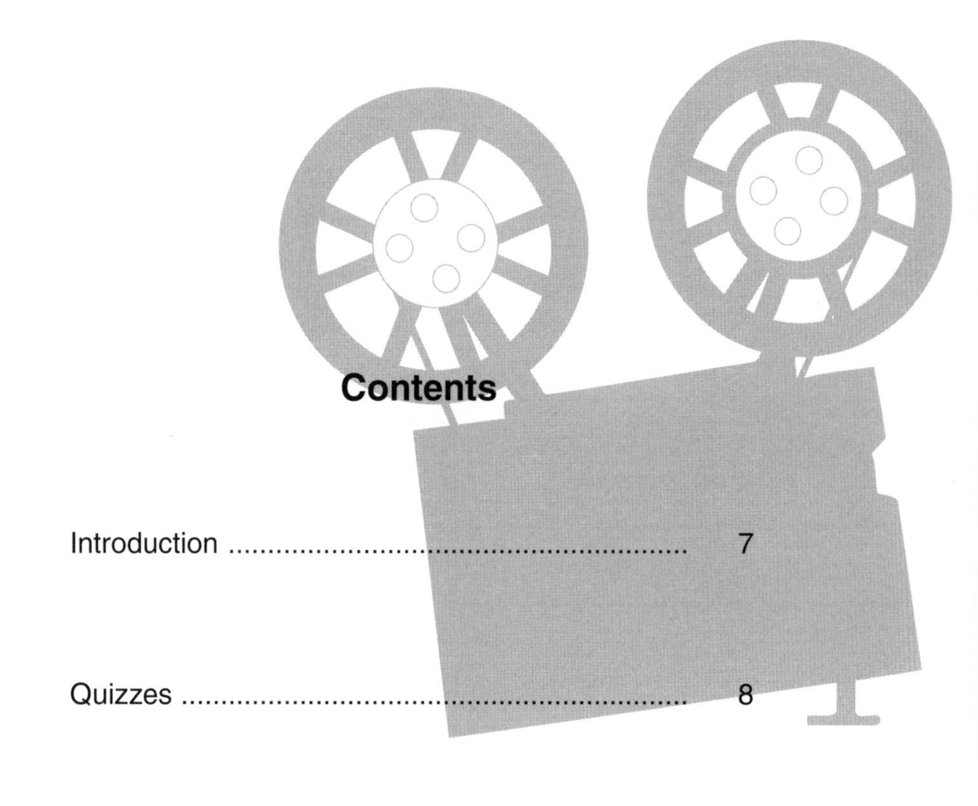

Contents

Introduction 7

Quizzes 8

Answers 142

The Hollywood Quiz Book is a celebration of the rich variety of entertainment brought to us by the movie industry. Each successive generation has produced its own cinema culture and so this book has been created to span virtually all eras and genres of movie, from the 1920s to the present day. Questions have been randomly mixed in respect of the year of release, etc, so that no matter what your age you will probably know the answer to several in each quiz. Some questions are hard and some are easy, but I hope all are interesting and entertaining.

Don't worry if you find that some names of movies, actors, actresses, genres etc, are unfamiliar; you can't know them all! Maybe certain new titles and names might just intrigue your curiosity into discovering new movies.

So sit back with family and friends and find out just how well you know your movies.

Eric Saunders

QUIZ 1

1. Which famous classic Hollywood movie finishes with the line "After all, tomorrow is another day"?

2. Which actor portrayed the driver in the Oscar-winning movie *Driving Miss Daisy?*

3. *The Magnificent Seven* featured Yul Brynner, Charles Bronson, Steve McQueen, James Coburn and Brad Dexter. Name the other two actors who made up the 'Seven'.

4. Which star, who died in July 1965, appeared in over 100 TV shows and 80 movies and then went on to be stuffed, mounted and put on display?

5. In which classic Hollywood movie did Humphrey Bogart portray the character Charlie Allnut?

6. Which blockbuster movie was the first to be based on a ride at Walt Disney World in Florida?

7. In which movie does Tom Hanks play a hit man called Michael Sullivan?

8. Who plays 'the Caped Crusader' in the 2008 Batman movie, *The Dark Knight*?

9 In *The Pink Panther*, the first movie to feature the bungling Inspector Clouseau, who or what was the Pink Panther?

10 Which Hitchcock movie had the tagline "It only takes one witness to spoil the perfect crime"?

11 The epic 'Bridge of Khazad-dûm' sequence takes place in which *Lord Of The Rings* movie?

12 Hollywood star Orlando Bloom made his big screen debut in the 1997 biopic *Wilde.* Who played the title role in this movie?

13 In which 1974 disaster movie would you hear the line "When are you architects going to learn?"?

14 What does the initial in the name of actor Samuel L Jackson stand for?

15 In which movie did Yul Brynner play a robot gunslinger who stalked the streets of a theme park?

16 Jack Nicholson won his first Best Actor Oscar for his part in which movie?

QUIZ 2

1 For which movie did Tom Hanks win an Oscar playing opposite a mute character called Wilson?

2 Who played the part of Harrison Ford's 'father' in the movie *Indiana Jones And The Last Crusade*?

3 In which movie did Dustin Hoffman play the part of Benjamin Braddock?

4 In which Hollywood musical is Billy Bigelow the central character?

5 In which acclaimed 1973 movie did Tatum O'Neal star with her father, Ryan?

6 Which American talk show host won an Academy Award in 1985 for her role in the movie *The Color Purple*?

7 In which Hitchcock movie does Bruno suggest killing Guy's wife in return for Guy killing Bruno's wife?

8 In which musical did Gene Kelly portray the actor Don Lockwood, who has problems with the squeaky-voiced actress Lina Lamont?

9 Which movie, starring Robert Redford and Dustin Hoffman, depicts events surrounding the Watergate scandal?

10 Which 1962 film starred Bette Davis and Joan Crawford as the Hudson sisters?

11 In which 1999 psychological thriller does a troubled boy, played by Haley Joel Osmont, say that he sees dead people?

12 In which film does Demi Moore shave her head for Uncle Sam?

13 Which actor, born in Vancouver in 1961, portrays Marty McFly in the movie *Back To The Future*?

14 *The Elephant Man* (1980), *Raging Bull* (1981) and *Young Frankenstein* (1974): what's the common link?

15 Which actor links the films *Predator 2* and *Lethal Weapon 2*?

16 Which Hollywood star's films were not allowed to be shown in Monaco?

QUIZ 3

1 Who portrayed the industrialist who saved hundreds of Jewish people from Nazi death camps in the Steven Spielberg movie, *Schindler's List*?

2 Which Oscar-winning western movie of 1992 starred Clint Eastwood and Gene Hackman?

3 Which 1958 science fiction horror movie marked Steve McQueen's big-screen debut?

4 In which movie does Julia Roberts portray a gutsy single mother who takes on a big corporation over water contamination?

5 Which early 20th century movie actress was known as 'America's Sweetheart'?

6 Which actor got 'stung' in the movie *The Sting*?

7 Who was the first black actor to become a major Hollywood star, appearing in films such as *To Sir With Love* and *In The Heat Of The Night*?

8 In which movie does a TV weatherman, played by Bill Murray, keep waking up to face February 2nd every day?

9 What was Harrison Ford's profession before he was picked up to be a movie actor?

10 Who portrayed Malcolm X in the movie of the same name?

11 When Loni Anderson appeared in the title role of the movie *The Jayne Mansfield Story*, which muscle man portrayed her husband?

12 The song *Raindrops Keep Falling On My Head,* featured in *Butch Cassidy And The Sundance Kid,* was written by which composer?

13 In which movie does Steve Martin appear as Neil Page, a man who is desperately trying to get home for Thanksgiving?

14 In which science fiction movie do blue-eyed boys ride sandworms on a parched planet?

15 Which well-known horror-movie star was born William Henry Pratt in London, England, in 1887?

16 Released in 1961, what was the final movie of both Marilyn Monroe and Clark Gable?

QUIZ 4

1. Which Cary Grant movie concerns two old ladies who invite men to their house and then poison them with home-made wine?

2. In the making of the first *Star Wars* movie, which actor wore carpet slippers because his boots were too tight?

3. Who is the only Oscar to have won an Oscar?

4. In which movie does Danny Kaye sing about "the vessel with the pestle with the pellet with the poison and the chalice from the palace with the brew which is true"?

5. In which movie do Clint Eastwood, Tommy Lee Jones, Donald Sutherland and James Garner all appear as astronauts?

6. Who starred as the juror who is not convinced of the alleged guilt of a teenager, in the movie *12 Angry Men*?

7. In which movie, as a call-girl does Jane Fonda say "For an hour I'm the best actress in the world"?

8. Which actor is trapped in a phone booth in the 2002 movie *Phone Booth*?

9 Which star of nearly 30 movies died in the arms of Jean Harlow at age 13?

10 Which actress was awarded an Oscar for her portrayal of a mute in the movie *The Piano*?

11 "If you build it he will come" are the mysterious words heard by Kevin Costner in which movie?

12 In which movie did Clint Eastwood first use the immortal line "Go ahead, make my day"?

13 How many Marx Brothers were there?

14 How many searchlights rake the sky in the Twentieth Century Fox logo?

15 What was the name of the character played by Sharon Stone in *Basic Instinct*?

16 Which movie character promises to stay "until the wind changes"?

QUIZ 5

1 Which movie actress was discovered, aged 15, in 1949 by the producer Carlo Ponti, who would later become her husband?

2 Which actor was married first to Jane Wyman and later to Nancy Davis?

3 Name the producer/director of movies such as *Dark Crystal* and *Teenage Mutant Ninja Turtles*, who died in 1990 just as he was about to sell his company to Disney.

4 Who or what was Blue Thunder, in the 1983 movie of that name?

5 What style of acting was taught by Lee Strasberg's Actors Studio?

6 Born Edda van Heemstra Hepburn-Ruston in Belgium in 1929, by what name is this person better known to movie audiences?

7 In which movie did Bob Hoskins play private detective Eddie Valiant?

8 Made in 1976, what was John Wayne's last movie?

9 Which actress' real name is Margaret Mary Emily Anne Hyra?

10 In which movie do John Travolta and Samuel L Jackson appear as a couple of hit men?

11 Who directed the Oscar-winning movie *Out Of Africa*?

12 *Family Plot* was the 54th and final movie by which director?

13 In which movie does Sean Connery play a thief opposite Catherine Zeta Jones?

14 In which movie does John Malkovitch appear as the character Cyrus 'The Virus'?

15 In which movie did Laurence Olivier torture Dustin Hoffman by drilling his teeth?

16 Who played Robert Stroud, aka the Birdman of Alcatraz, in the 1962 movie of that name?

QUIZ 6

1. What was the name of the nightclub where Sam played piano, in the movie *Casablanca*?

2. What was Alfred Hitchcock's first Hollywood movie, which won the Best Picture Oscar in 1940?

3. In the Hitchcock thriller *Frenzy* what was the serial killer's murder weapon?

4. What was the Oscar-winning song from *Breakfast At Tiffany's*?

5. Who starred as the serial killer Aileen Wuornos in the 2003 movie *Monster*?

6. The *Nostromo* was the name of the spaceship in which space horror movie of 1979?

7. In which movie does Dan Aykroyd rampage though a Christmas party wearing a Santa Claus outfit and waving a gun?

8. What did Bette Davis give Joan Crawford for breakfast in a notorious scene in *Whatever Happened To Baby Jane*?

9 In which movie, based on a Stephen King novel, are a woman and her young son trapped in their car by a rabid dog?

10 "He comes at you with a knife, you go after him with a gun, he puts one of yours in hospital, you put one of his in the morgue. That's the Chicago way." In which movie does Sean Connery make this speech?

11 Which singer did Diana Ross portray in the movie *Lady Sings The Blues*?

12 What did Bob Hope, Stuart Granger and Cary Grant all have in common?

13 What was the name of Anthony Hopkins' character in *Silence Of The Lambs*?

14 Which American singer/actress won an Academy Award in 1987 for her role in *Moonstruck*?

15 Which actor provided the voice of Darth Vader in the original *Star Wars* movies?

16 *When You Wish Upon A Star* was a song first featured in which Disney movie?

QUIZ 7

1. Who played Amity Island's police chief in the first *Jaws* movie?

2. Which comedy actor read the bible on his death-bed – claiming that he was "looking for loopholes"?

3. Which actress, who made her screen debut in *Our Dancing Daughters,* was born Lucille LeSueur?

4. In the Disney animated movie *The Jungle Book,* what kind of creature was Shere Khan?

5. Who was the only actor to appear in both *The Dirty Dozen* and *The Magnificent Seven*?

6. In which movie does Robert Redford go out for a sandwich and on his return find all his work colleagues murdered?

7. In which 1961 movie does Paul Newman play the part of 'Fast Eddie' Felson?

8. Clint Eastwood was the mayor of which Californian town from 1986-88?

9 In which movie did Shirley Temple sing *On The Good Ship Lollipop*?

10 How many *Road To ...* movies, starring Bob Hope and Bing Crosby, were made?

11 Which black comedy movie of 1991 was based on a 1960s TV series which in turn was based on a series of cartoons in *The New Yorker* magazine?

12 Which Alfred Hitchcock movie first featured the song *Que Sera Sera*, sung by Doris Day?

13 Which 1988 comedy horror movie, starring Michael Keaton, featured the famous *Banana Boat Song,* sung by Harry Belafonte?

14 In which 1971 movie does Clint Eastwood play a wounded Civil War soldier who takes refuge in a girls' school?

15 Which famous screen lover died, aged 31, on August 23rd 1926 due to complications following surgery for a stomach ulcer?

16 Daddy Warbucks, a munitions factory owner, appears in which 1982 musical movie?

QUIZ 8

1. Released in 2004, what is the title of the third *Harry Potter* movie?

2. What kind of creature is Iago in the Disney animated movie *Aladdin*?

3. Who starred in the title role in the 1962 boxing-themed movie, *Kid Galahad*?

4. Which 1942 movie starred James Cagney as song-and-dance man George M Cohan?

5. In which black comedy movie does Peter Sellers play three different characters: a British pilot, the American president and a wheelchair-bound ex-Nazi who forgets not to give the 'Heil Hitler' salute?

6. Which actress reputedly took 59 attempts to say the line "Where's the bourbon?" during the making of *Some Like It Hot*?

7. Who, in a 1997 movie, "protected the Earth from the scum of the universe"?

8. In which movie do Keanu Reeves and Alex Winter take on Death in a variety of games?

9 Which 1967 movie was tagged with 'They're young, they're in love, they kill people'?

10 Who was the first screen actor to refuse an Academy Award?

11 At the end of which movie does Steve McQueen return to solitary confinement in a POW camp; his escape by motorcycle having failed?

12 What was Norman Bates' hobby in the Hitchcock movie *Psycho*?

13 Who directed the 2000 movie *Crouching Tiger, Hidden Dragon*?

14 Which famous Hollywood movie-maker directed the first ever episode of TV's *Columbo*?

15 In the 1939 movie, *The Wizard Of Oz,* which part was played by Bert Lahr?

16 In which courtroom drama movie does Jack Nicholson, as Colonel Nathan Jessep, say "You can't handle the truth"?

QUIZ 9

1 Directed by Bernardo Bertolucci, which biopic movie won nine Oscars in 1988?

2 Which South African activist's death was the subject of the 1987 movie *Cry Freedom*?

3 In the movie *Shrek,* who provided the voice of Shrek?

4 Which Mel Brookes spoof Western movie features a black sheriff and Yiddish-speaking Indians?

5 In which 2002 movie does Robin Williams portray a man with a dark side who works in a darkroom?

6 In which movie does Tom Cruise make a peanut-butter sandwich for 'daughter' (Dakota Fanning) only to be told by her that she has a peanut allergy?

7 What is the name of the killer in the *Nightmare On Elm Street* series of movies?

8 Which movie company was formed in 1919 by Douglas Fairbanks, Mary Pickford, Charlie Chaplin and D W Griffith?

9 Which country banned Spielberg's *E.T.* for children under 11 years because of scenes showing children disobeying their parents?

10 Which movie brought the talents of Anthony Hopkins and Anne Bancroft together in 1986?

11 Fanny Brice was the main character in which 1968 musical movie, starring Barbra Streisand and Omar Sharif?

12 What is Woody Allen's real name?

13 The brand name of RKO is familiar to most people. What do the initials RKO represent?

14 In *Close Encounters Of The Third Kind*, which French movie director appears as the scientist, Lacombe?

15 In which European city was the first feature movie shown to a paying audience, in December 1895?

16 In which movie does a writer assault his greatest fan with a typewriter?

QUIZ 10

1. Who won an Oscar for his portrayal of Lester Burnham in the movie *American Beauty*?

2. What does Charlton Heston find partly buried in the closing sequence of the 1968 movie *Planet Of The Apes*?

3. Who played George Clooney's character's ex-wife in the 2001 movie *Ocean's Eleven*?

4. *The Cocoanuts* (1929) was the first movie to feature which comedy team?

5. What was the name of the hotel in the Jack Nicholson movie *The Shining*?

6. *The Greek Tycoon* of 1978 was vaguely based on the lives of which famous couple?

7. During a scene in a movie theater, which famous Disney movie is being watched by the creatures in *The Gremlins*?

8. Who won the best actress Oscar in 1984 for her part in the movie *Terms Of Endearment*?

9 'Fear can hold you prisoner, hope can set you free' was the tagline for which movie of 1994?

10 What was the first name of Mrs Doubtfire in the 1993 movie of the same title?

11 Who or what was 'baby' in the 1938 movie, *Bringing Up Baby*?

12 In which movie does Marilyn Monroe's skirt billow up over a grating on a New York street?

13 Who plays Sirius Black in the *Harry Potter* movies?

14 In which chick-flick do Geena Davis and Susan Sarandon hit the road in a 1966 Ford Thunderbird?

15 Completed shortly before his death in 1999, what was the last movie to be directed by Stanley Kubrick?

16 In which movie does Dustin Hoffman portray an autistic man who is a whizz at blackjack?

QUIZ 11

1 Which 1994 movie relates the true story of the rigging of a 1950s popular TV trivia contest?

2 Which *Star Trek* regular directed the movie *Three Men And A Baby*?

3 Which movie, starring Jodie Foster and Kelly McGillis has the tag line 'The first scream was for help, the second is for justice'?

4 What was the name of Kevin Costner's native American wife in the movie *Dances With Wolves*?

5 In which famous movie scene does Paul Henreid light two cigarettes; one for himself and one for Bette Davis?

6 Which Spielberg movie relates the story of an 11-year-old boy in a Japanese internment camp?

7 In which 1980 movie does Robert Redford play the part of a prison chief who goes undercover to investigate brutality in the prison he is going to run?

8 In which movie does Rebecca de Mornay play the psycho-nanny from hell?

9 Which gunslinger was portrayed by Paul Newman in the 1958 movie *The Left-Handed Gun*?

10 In which Brian de Palma thriller did Michael Caine play a psychopathic killer in drag?

11 What is the name of the hunter who always just fails to get Bugs Bunny?

12 Regarded by many as the best western movie ever made, John Wayne is on the trail of his kidnapped niece, played by Natalie Wood, in which 1956 movie?

13 Who received an Oscar for his portrayal of a young priest in a New York slum district, in the 1944 movie *Going My Way*?

14 In which movie does Gene Kelly dance with an animated Jerry Mouse?

15 Which French actor portrayed Christopher Columbus in the movie *1492*?

16 In 1981, when Miles O'Keefe played Tarzan, who played Jane?

QUIZ 12

1. In the movie *My Stepmother Is An Alien*, who played the stepmother?

2. Which movie role caused actor Buddy Ebsen to be hospitalized due to being covered in greasepaint and aluminum dust each day?

3. In which movie do you hear the famous line, spoken in a diner, "I'll have what she's having"?

4. In which movie does Clint Eastwood first appear as 'The Man With No Name'?

5. Which character was portrayed by Dooley Wilson in *Casablanca*?

6. After being radioactively contaminated, Grant Williams was physically reduced in which movie of 1957?

7. The 1953 biblical epic *The Robe* was the first production to employ which movie format?

8. In the Alfred Hitchcock movie *The Trouble With Harry*, what exactly was the trouble with Harry?

9 Who was the stop-motion expert whose special effects can be seen in adventure movies such as *Jason And The Argonauts*?

10 Who portrayed 'a man called Horse', in the 1970 movie of the same name?

11 Made just before his death, what was the last movie starring Peter Sellers, in which he plays an illiterate gardener?

12 In which movie did Kirk Douglas portray the artist Vincent Van Gogh?

13 What kind of creatures attacked Melanie Griffith's (real-life) mother in a 1963 Hitchcock movie?

14 In which movie did Greta Garbo first speak the immortal line "I want to be alone" – a trademark quote ever since?

15 The studio report on whom apparently stated "Can't act, can't sing, can dance a little"?

16 Which Hollywood actress married Prince Rainier III of Monaco in 1956?

QUIZ 13

1. Who portrays the Incredible Shrinking Woman in the movie of the same name?

2. In which Marx Brothers movie did the character Rufus T Firefly appear?

3. The science fiction novel *Do Androids Dream Of Electric Sheep?* was the basis for which movie, starring Harrison Ford?

4. The beginning of which movie featured a cigar-smoking baby (Baby Herman)?

5. What was Eddie Murphy's first feature movie?

6. In regard to Academy Awards, for what is Margaret Herrick remembered?

7. In 1982, the best original song Oscar went to *Up Where We Belong*. In which movie did it feature?

8. What was the name of the ship's cat in the science fiction thriller movie *Alien?*

9 What is the full title of the *Borat* movie which took America by storm in 2006?

10 In which movie does Jeff Goldblum play the part of Seth Brundle, a man who becomes hideously deformed when an experiment goes wrong?

11 In which movie, also starring Ann-Margret and Burgess Meredith, does Anthony Hopkins portray a ventriloquist who becomes dominated by his dummy – a foul-mouthed character called Fats?

12 In *The Addams Family*, the children are named Pugsley and Wednesday. What are the names of their parents?

13 In which Hitchcock thriller does James Stewart witness a murder whilst confined to his apartment by a broken leg?

14 "I'm ready for my close-up, Mr DeMille" is the last line from which classic 1950 movie?

15 Which 1960 comedy horror movie features a plant with a liking for human flesh?

16 Who directed the Oscar-winning movie *Forrest Gump*?

QUIZ 14

1. In which movie does Melanie Griffith say that she had "a head for business and a body for sin"?

2. In which 1982 movie does Meryl Streep portray a Polish death-camp survivor?

3. In which movie does Arnold Schwarzenegger play the character Jack Slater?

4. Tom Cruise plays the wheelchair-bound Vietnam veteran Ron Kovic in which movie of 1989?

5. Which famous Mel Brookes comedy movie features the song *Springtime For Hitler*?

6. Nicole Kidman plays a ruthless TV weather girl in which 1995 movie, also starring Matt Dillon?

7. Who directed the Oscar-winning *Midnight Cowboy*?

8. Who portrayed Michael Douglas' wife in the movie *Fatal Attraction*?

9 When the prized mascot of the Miami Dolphins is kidnapped, who comes to the rescue?

10 In which movie does Jim Carrey use his newly-acquired powers to enhance the size of Jennifer Aniston's bust-line?

11 In which 2005 movie does Jodie Foster find that her daughter is missing on a flight from Berlin to New York?

12 Which 2005 science fiction movie was an extension of the canceled Fox TV series *Firefly*?

13 On which pop music star did Johnny Depp base his Captain Jack Sparrow character in *Pirates Of The Caribbean*?

14 In which movie does Tony Curtis play Albert De Salvo, a murderer who poses as a handyman?

15 Which movie starts with the entire British royal family being wiped out in a freak accident, leaving John Goodman to take over as king?

16 What was the name of the character who met a nasty end in the shower in the movie *Psycho*?

QUIZ 15

1 Oda Mae Brown was Whoopi Goldberg's character in which romantic thriller movie of 1990?

2 Movie actors Alan Rickman, Tom Baker and Christopher Lee have all played which insane religious character?

3 Who played Princess Leia in the early *Star Wars* movies?

4 Erich Maria Remarque wrote which anti-war novel on which two (1930 and 1979) movies of the same title, were based?

5 Which actor starred in and directed the movie *The Horse Whisperer*?

6 What kind of creature was Gertie, the subject of one the first animated movies, made in 1914?

7 What was the name of Elliott's older brother in *E.T.*?

8 Whose movie scores include the music for *Planet Of The Apes*, *Papillon*, *The Omen* and several of the *Star Trek* movies?

9 Meryl Streep, Pierce Brosnan, Amanda Seyfried and Colin Firth all appeared in which 2008 musical movie?

10 In which movie did Paul Newman keep asking "Who are those guys"?

11 Which famous movie actor was born Bernard Schwartz?

12 Who was Carrie Fisher's first husband?

13 Hitchcock's 1954 *Rear Window* was remade for TV in 1998. Who starred as the wheelchair-bound main character, Jason Kemp, in the remake?

14 Who created, and portrayed, Austin Powers?

15 Which writer of children's books created the character The Grinch?

16 Which 'doctor', created by novelist Max Brand, and familiar to 1960s TV audiences, made several movie appearances in the 1930s and 40s, set in the environs of 'Blair Hospital'?

QUIZ 16

1. In which 1941 movie does Bette Davis portray the Southern aristocrat Regina Giddens?

2. "I love the fresh smell of napalm in the morning" is a famous line from which 1979 movie?

3. "Sooner or later everyone does ..." meet whom, the title of a movie starring Brad Pitt?

4. Which movie, based on a novel by Gaston Leroux, and set in Paris, France, has had four different versions made (in 1925, 1943, 1962 and 1982)?

5. Which ubiquitous screen character was born of a novel, *First Blood,* by David Morrell?

6. Starring Geena Davis and Jeff Goldblum, which 1988 comedy movie tells of three aliens who absorb knowledge of planet Earth via TV programs?

7. Which famous one-time conductor of the Philadelphia Orchestra appeared in Walt Disney's *Fantasia*?

8. Which 1925 Charlie Chaplin movie shows the little man successfully prospecting for gold in the Yukon?

9 Which twice-made (1962 and 1997) movie, the earlier one directed by Stanley Kubrick, was based on a novel by Vladimir Nabokov?

10 Which beauty pageant is threatened by terrorists in *Miss Congeniality*, a movie of 2000?

11 What was the silly mistake in the title of the 1968 movie *Krakatoa, East Of Java*?

12 The story to which 1959 movie, starring Charlton Heston, was adapted to an animated movie version, featuring Heston's voice, in 2003?

13 Starring Bruce Willis, which 1996 movie is about Irish versus Italian gang warfare in Texas during the Prohibition era?

14 Starring Steve McQueen and Faye Dunaway in 1968, which movie was remade in 1999 – this time starring Pierce Brosnan and Rene Russo?

15 Who wrote the score for the 1997 movie *Titanic*?

16 Which rock band was the subject of Martin Scorsese's movie *The Last Waltz*?

QUIZ 17

1. Which epic movie of 1965, starring Omar Sharif in the title role, was based on a Boris Pasternak novel?

2. The 1970 movie *Song Of Norway* was based on the life of which composer?

3. Who wrote the screenplay, directed, produced and narrated the classic movie *The Magnificent Ambersons*?

4. Who starred as Sherman McCoy in *Bonfire Of The Vanities*?

5. Who starred as law graduate Mitch McDeere in the 1993 version of *The Firm*?

6. Who stars as the clumsy police lieutenant, Frank Drebin, in the *Naked Gun* movies?

7. Which 2000 movie relates the story of the fishing boat *Andrea Gail* and her crew?

8. Which 1968 movie stars Jack Lemmon and Walter Matthau as two TV men who share an apartment?

9 In Disney's *Fantasia,* which character plays the part of the Sorcerer's Apprentice?

10 Which 1984 science fiction comedy movie involves three parapsychologists who save New York from malevolent spirits?

11 *Giant,* the 1956 movie starring Elizabeth Taylor and Rock Hudson, was the last movie appearance in a leading role, of which actor before his untimely death?

12 *The Longest Day* is a 1962 movie about which specific event of Word War II?

13 Which novel by Anthony Hope has been made into six different movie versions; the 1937 version with Douglas Fairbanks Jr probably being the best?

14 In a 2001 movie, which ogre, who likes a quiet life, finds his swamp invaded by exiled fairy-tale people?

15 Who or what was Flicka in the movie *My Friend Flicka*?

16 Which 1950s science fiction movie, starring Walter Pidgeon and Anne Francis, featured Robby the Robot?

QUIZ 18

1 Which Beau Geste-esque movie of 1931 starred Laurel and Hardy?

2 Which 'cult' movie of 2000 starred Melanie Griffith in the role of the mean-spirited Honey Whitlock?

3 Who starred as the left-behind kid in *Home Alone*?

4 *To Die For* and *Batman Forever* both featured which actress?

5 In Disney's *Jungle Book* what was the name of the jazz music-loving bear?

6 In the first *Toy Story* what was the name of the child who owns all the toys?

7 Which famous Wagnerian music is featured in *Apocalypse Now*?

8 Which actress is the daughter of Peter Fonda?

9 In which movie does Liza Minnelli play the part of dancer Sally Bowles?

10 For their roles in which movie did Vivien Leigh win Best Actress and Hattie McDaniel win Best Supporting Actress Oscars?

11 Who sang *Unchained Melody* in the movie *Ghost*?

12 *The Sound Of Music* is set in which European country?

13 Who wrote the music for *West Side Story*?

14 What are Si and Am in the Disney animated movie *Lady And The Tramp*?

15 Who played the part of Peter Pan in the movie *Hook*?

16 Which married screen couple starred in the 1947 movie *Dark Passage*?

QUIZ 19

1 Which Scorsese-directed 1990 movie was based on the novel *Wise Guy* by Nicholas Pileggi?

2 Which baseball star married Marilyn Monroe in 1954?

3 *My Man* was the closing song, and the original title, of which 1968 movie based on a Broadway play?

4 In *The Flintstones* movie, which character was played by Rick Moranis?

5 What was unusual about Otto, the 'automatic pilot', in the movie *Airplane!*?

6 Which 1999 D-Day landing story movie was directed and produced by Steven Spielberg?

7 Which actress appeared in *High Noon* and *Rear Window*?

8 Which Tennessee Williams play has been adapted into a movie three times, the earliest (1951) starring Marlon Brando and Vivien Leigh?

9 Who was the female star of the 1960 movie *Butterfield 8*?

10 The movie *Jurassic Park* was based on the novel of the same name by which author?

11 *Plane Crazy, The Gallopin' Gaucho* and *Steamboat Willie* were the first movies to feature which cartoon character?

12 Which 1972 comedy movie starred Ryan O'Neal and Barbra Streisand?

13 What was the name of the German *femme fatale,* played by Madeline Kahn, in *Blazing Saddles*?

14 Who grew his hair and a beard to go undercover as Serpico in the movie of 1973?

15 In 1981, which actress accidentally drowned during the time she was engaged in the filming of the science fiction movie *Brainstorm*?

16 Who received Best Actor Oscars for his performances in *High Noon* and *Sergeant York*?

QUIZ 20

1 Who played the leading female role in *Air Force One*?

2 As what does Whoopi Goldberg dress up in the movie, *Sister Act*?

3 Which character did Mark Hamill portray in the first *Star Wars* movie?

4 What is the name of the family in *The Omen* movies?

5 Which 2004 movie, based on a 1970s TV series, starred Ben Stiller and Owen Wilson in the title roles?

6 Based on a novel by Ira Levin, which 1969 horror movie starred Mia Farrow?

7 Which 1998 space movie, based on a 1960s TV series, starred Gary Oldman as Dr Zachary Smith?

8 *The Rose*, starring Bette Midler, is a biopic loosely based on the showbiz life of which rock singer who died in 1970?

9 Which famous singer played a major role in the 1953 movie *From Here To Eternity*?

10 Created by cartoonist Robert Crumb, which comic book character made it onto the big screen in an animated movie of 1971?

11 What is Goldie Hawn's real name?

12 Which star actor did much of his own driving stunt work in the famous car chase in the 1968 movie *Bullitt*?

13 *Catch 22,* the 1970 movie based on the novel by Joseph Heller, is set during which war?

14 Scarlett O'Hara is the fictional leading female character of which movie?

15 Whose first major movie role was the part of Billy Nolan in the horror movie *Carrie*?

16 Who played the part of The Joker in the 1989 *Batman* movie?

QUIZ 21

1. Who portrayed Jonathan E, the hero in the 1975 movie *Rollerball*?

2. From which 1980 comedy movie does the following line come: "There's no reason to be alarmed and we hope you enjoy your flight ... by the way, is there anyone on board who knows how to fly a plane?"?

3. The 2001 movie, *Black Hawk Down,* is based on real events surrounding a military helicopter mission over which African city?

4. What is the title of the second movie of the *Lord Of The Rings* trilogy?

5. Who composed the scores for many western movies, including *The Magnificent Seven*?

6. Which Ukrainian-born composer wrote the scores to *The Fall Of The Roman Empire, The Alamo* and *Mr Smith Goes To Washington*?

7. In which movie of 2002 does Matt Damon play a CIA agent with amnesia?

8. What was the first movie to be directed by John Huston, in 1941?

9 Actress Julie Andrews married which American movie director/producer in 1969?

10 *Happy Talk* and *Bali Ha'i* are two of the many songs from which 1958 movie musical?

11 Based on a novel by Nevil Shute, which 1959 movie has Gregory Peck and Ava Gardner waiting for the end, following World War III?

12 *The Sentinel,* an early short story by Arthur C Clarke, was the basis for which epic science fiction movie?

13 What was the name of the detective, played by Humphrey Bogart, in *The Maltese Falcon*?

14 Which female director was Oscar-nominated for her 2003 movie *Lost In Translation*?

15 Who won the Best Actor Oscar in 2004 for his part in the movie *Ray*?

16 Which movie actress said "Hollywood is a place where they'll pay you $1,000 for a kiss and 50 cents for your soul"?

QUIZ 22

1. Who turned down the part to hand Eddie Murphy top billing in *Beverly Hills Cop*?

2. Which famous redhead portrayed Virginia Brush in the 1941 movie *Strawberry Blonde*?

3. The song, *Hopelessly Devoted To You,* featured in which movie?

4. In the movie *Little Shop Of Horrors,* which two words are the only ones spoken by the human-eating plant?

5. In which movie does Dustin Hoffman play a prisoner incarcerated on Devil's Island?

6. Which actor appeared in both *Parenthood* and *Ghostbusters*?

7. Who played the male lead opposite Nicole Kidman in the movie *The Peacemaker*?

8. To which movie director was Sharon Tate married at the time of her murder in 1969?

9 What was the title of the sequel to *Jurassic Park*?

10 What was the title of the sequel to *2001: A Space Odyssey*?

11 What was the title of the sequel to the 1970 movie *Love Story*?

12 Which French movie director (1928-2000) was married to Jane Fonda and Brigitte Bardot?

13 Which actress' first two husbands were Gary Oldman and Ethan Hawke?

14 Who won the 1967 Best Actress Oscar for her part in *Guess Who's Coming To Dinner*?

15 'The Inventor' who gave Edward his 'scissor hands' in the 1990 movie, was played by which veteran actor?

16 In which American state does the story of *The Blair Witch Project* take place?

QUIZ 23

1. Who was Mrs Michael Douglas before Catherine Zeta Jones?

2. Which Dracula 'lookalike' starred in the first movie of that title (in 1931)?

3. What kind of creature was Keiko in the movie *Free Willy*?

4. What was the title of the 1963 Disney movie, based on a novel by Sheila Burnford, that told the story of a trio of animals who cross the wilderness in search of their owner?

5. What is Brad Pitt's real first name?

6. What breed of dog starred alongside James Belushi in the movie *K9*?

7. What kind of peak is the subject of *Dante's Peak,* the 1997 disaster movie starring Pierce Brosnan?

8. For his part in which 1995 movie did Nicolas Cage win the Best Actor Oscar?

9 Which 1995 movie has the famous line "Houston, we have a problem"?

10 Who made his big-screen debut at age eight in *Back To The Future II*, later starring in the title role of Disney's *Adventures Of Huck Finn*?

11 Which British actor starred in *Santa Claus: The Movie* and *Arthur*?

12 Who starred in the title role of the 1989 *Batman* movie?

13 Which actor played the part of Willie Bank in the 2007 movie *Ocean's 13*?

14 Which movie composer has held chief conductor posts with symphony orchestras in London, Los Angeles, Houston and Oslo?

15 In which 1987 movie does Olympia Dukakis play Cher's 'mother'?

16 Which actress plays a stalker obsessed with the radio DJ, portrayed by Clint Eastwood, in *Play Misty For Me*?

QUIZ 24

1 In which movie does Robert De Niro portray the character Mike Vronsky?

2 Which famous singer appeared with Warren Beatty in the *Dick Tracey* movie?

3 Which famous screen couple starred in the 1965 movie *The Sandpiper*?

4 *Duel*, a 1971 movie starring Dennis Weaver, was the first feature-length movie of which director?

5 Which actress played the lead female role, Lynn Bracken, in *LA Confidential*?

6 By what stage name was Leonard Slye better known?

7 Which daughter of Ryan O'Neal was the youngest actress ever to win an Oscar, in 1974?

8 R2D2 and C3PO are robots from which series of movies?

9 Who played the main male lead opposite Julie Andrews in *Mary Poppins*?

10 Which swashbuckling hero of the silver screen made his mark with a Z-shape slash of his sword?

11 Which German actress was the star of the 1930 movie *The Blue Angel*?

12 Which world is inhabited by Traders, Atoll-Dwellers, Smokers and Slavers in a Kevin Costner movie of 1995?

13 Tom Hanks, Kelsey Grammer, Tim Allen and Joan Cusack were among those heard but never seen in which animated sequel of 1999?

14 The action in the movie *Braveheart* takes place in which country?

15 In *Close Encounters Of The Third Kind,* what is found in the Sonoran desert at the beginning of the movie?

16 Which play by William Shakespeare is the basis for the 1961 movie, *West Side Story*?

QUIZ 25

1 In which movie, directed by her father, John, did Anjelica Huston make her big-screen debut in 1969?

2 Which 1997 science fiction action movie was based on a novel of the same name by Robert Heinlein?

3 Which land of myth and legend is the home of the alien race in the movie *Cocoon*?

4 *The Fastest Guitar Alive,* a western movie of 1967, starred which pop singer?

5 *Nosferatu,* a German silent movie made in 1921, was the first movie to feature which horror figure?

6 What was the title of the 1996 movie, starring Julia Roberts in the title role, that was a reworking of the Jekyll and Hyde tale?

7 Which famous reclusive industrialist was the 1961 novel, and the subsequent 1964 movie, *The Carpetbaggers,* allegedly based on?

8 On which Canadian writer's novel is the movie *The English Patient* based?

9 In which 1995 romantic comedy does Sandra Bullock play the part of a fare-collector on Chicago's overhead railway?

10 In which 1973 movie, set in a bleak New York of the future, does Charlton Heston's character make a startling discovery about the food on offer?

11 In which 1996 movie does Jeff Goldblum play his part in the saving of planet Earth as the computer expert David Levinson?

12 Which director is famous for making a brief and anonymous appearance in each of his movies?

13 Who stars as Bruce Willis' assistant, Zeus Carver, in the *Die Hard* movies?

14 What was the name of Gene Hackman's character in the *French Connection* movies?

15 In 1982, which movie actor, with his friend A E Hotchner, founded a food company that donates all profits, after tax, to charity?

16 Which statesman is the assassination target in *Day Of The Jackal*?

QUIZ 26

1 Who won a best director Oscar for the movie *The Quiet Man*?

2 Who once said that his gravestone should have the inscription "On the whole, I'd rather be in Philadelphia"?

3 Who played the male lead in the 1962 movie *To Kill A Mockingbird*?

4 Complete the title of this Dustin Hoffman movie: *Who Is Harry Kellerman And ...*

5 The action in the movie *Don't Look Now,* starring Donald Sutherland and Julie Christie, mostly takes place in which European city?

6 In which movie did Sigourney Weaver portray the naturalist Dian Fossey?

7 In which 1983 movie did Woody Allen play the part of a human chameleon?

8 In which cult-status comedy movie does Jeff Bridges play the character known as 'The Dude'?

9 What was the name of Looney Tunes' amorous skunk with a French accent?

10 What is the name of the bad-tempered cowboy character with a big red beard who often appears in Bugs Bunny cartoons?

11 Who were the two leading characters, played by Jon Voight and Dustin Hoffmann, in *Midnight Cowboy*?

12 *The Good, The Bad And The Ugly* is a perfect example of which movie sub-genre?

13 Gregory Peck starred as Captain Ahab in which sea-faring movie of 1956?

14 The opening theme of the symphonic poem *Also Sprach Zarathustra,* by Richard Strauss, was made famous by its inclusion in which science fiction movie of 1968?

15 What are the names of Donald Duck's three mischievous nephews?

16 Who takes over William Shatner's duties at the helm in the 11th *Star Trek* movie, released in 2009?

QUIZ 27

1. Which famous dancer, a former co-star of Fred Astaire and Gene Kelly, died in Los Angeles in June 2008 at the age of 86?

2. Which duo wrote the songs for the movie *Oklahoma!*?

3. What is the title of the novel written by actress Carrie Fisher and made into a 1990 movie with the same title, starring Meryl Streep?

4. Who played the part of Aragorn in *The Lord Of The Rings* trilogy?

5. How is secret agent Simon Templar, the hero in a 1997 movie starring Val Kilmer, better known?

6. In which 1984 movie does a teenager join a martial arts club to help him stand up to the local gang?

7. Which world-famous singer appeared (as himself) in the black-comedy horror movie *Mars Attacks!*?

8. In which cult psychological thriller movie of 2001 is the hero almost killed when an airplane engine crashes into his bedroom?

9 Which star played the part of Roger 'Verbal' Kint in *The Usual Suspects*, a crime-noir movie of 1995?

10 In which movie does Keanu Reeves portray a computer programmer who goes by the alias 'Neo'?

11 In the 2007 *Simpsons* movie, which animal character appears in a baker's hat to promote a new hamburger? He has a creepy song named after him which got to No 3 in the Irish singles chart.

12 Who starred as the vampire hunter Eric Brooks in the *Blade* trilogy of horror movies?

13 For which 1994 Tarantino movie poster does Uma Thurman appear on a bed, smoking a cigarette and reading a book?

14 According to the 2007 movie's title, which American state is *No Country For Old Men*?

15 What is the title of the first Indiana Jones movie?

16 What is the title of the fourth Indiana Jones movie?

QUIZ 28

1. Then aged six years, which actress starred as Gertie in *E.T.: The Extraterrestrial*?

2. What is the stage name of Caryn Elaine Johnson?

3. Which star did Rhea Perlman, Carla Tortelli in TV's *Cheers,* marry in 1982?

4. Who stars in the title role in the 2008 action movie, *Hancock*?

5. Marilyn Monroe and Arthur Miller divorced at the time of the release of which Monroe movie?

6. Which part was played by Daniel Day-Lewis in the 1992 movie *The Last Of The Mohicans*?

7. What nickname did Jane Fonda acquire during the 1970s as a result of her opposition to American involvement in Vietnam?

8. To which movie actor was supermodel Cindy Crawford married from 1991– 95?

9 Who plays the part of Captain Corelli in *Captain Corelli's Mandolin*?

10 Who plays Captain Corelli's love-interest, Pelagia, in *Captain Corelli's Mandolin*?

11 What breed of dog appears in the title role of the *Beethoven* movies series?

12 Which sea-disaster movie of 1972 starred Leslie Nielsen as Captain Harrison and Gene Hackman as Reverend Frank Scott?

13 Elizabeth Parsons finally kills her husband, Nick, *after* serving a six-year prison sentence for his murder, in which movie of 1999?

14 Steve Martin starred in which 1996 movie that was based on a 1950s TV show starring Phil Silvers?

15 Which novel by Mary Shelley has been turned into at least 20 different horror movies?

16 Warren Beatty and Robert Redford were considered for which movie role, before it finally went to Dustin Hoffman?

QUIZ 29

1. Lana Turner, Bette Davis, Barbara Stanwyck and Carole Lombard were all considered for which screen role before it was given to Vivien Leigh?

2. Which 1982 Best Picture Oscar-winning biopic has the reputation of having the greatest-ever number of extras in the cast – approximately 300,000?

3. What is the name of the fish in the 1988 comedy movie starring Jamie Lee Curtis and John Cleese?

4. Which actress portrayed 'Easy' Iris Steensma in the movie *Taxi Driver*?

5. Who played the jewel thief in the 1981 movie *Thief*, which also starred Tuesday Weld?

6. Which two actors were top of the bill in *Holiday Inn* of 1942?

7. In which 1981 movie, starring Candice Bergen and Jacqueline Bisset, does Meg Ryan portray an 18-year-old girl?

8. Which studio produced the 1999 animated movie *Tarzan*?

9 Which 1984 movie, set in 1920s/30s New York, stars Robert De Niro as a Jewish gangster, David 'Noodles' Aaronson?

10 In which South American country did Butch Cassidy and The Sundance Kid meet their deaths?

11 Which famous redhead once said "I've never thought of myself as a sex goddess, more a comedienne who could dance"?

12 Starring Candice Bergen and Peter Strauss, which controversial 1970 movie was based on the Sand Creek, Colorado massacre of 1864?

13 In which movie did Julie Andrews play the role of actress Gertrude Lawrence?

14 Which actress appeared in both (1968 and 1999) versions of *The Thomas Crown Affair*?

15 'Saving the world is a hell of a job' is the tagline to which 2008 movie, starring Ron Perlman in the title role?

16 *Mommie Dearest* is a 1981 biopic about which Hollywood star actress?

QUIZ 30

1 The plot of *The Hunt For Red October* involves submarines belonging to which two nations?

2 What is the only movie that Alfred Hitchcock made twice (in 1934 and 1956)?

3 Which 1972 futuristic movie has Bruce Dern carefully tending Earth's last few remaining trees on board the spaceship *Valley Forge*?

4 Which British actor died before the completion of *Gladiator* (2000), necessitating CGI imagery being used to 'fill in' some of his scenes?

5 In which movie did Harrison Ford make an early appearance as the Stetson-wearing street-racer Bob Falfa?

6 *Gunfight At The OK Corral* (1957) featured which future *Star Trek* actor in the part of Morgan Earp?

7 Starring Jack Lemmon and Shirley MacLaine, which Billy Wilder-directed movie won the 1960 Best Picture Oscar?

8 During which conflict is the movie *Platoon,* set?

9 Who played the part of Sister Helen Prejean in the 1995 movie *Dead Man Walking*?

10 Which movie icon starred as Cal Trask in *East Of Eden?*

11 In which movie did Bruce Willis make his debut in 1987?

12 What is Julie Andrews holding in each of her hands as she romps over the Austrian countryside in the original poster for *The Sound Of Music*?

13 For which movie did Bob Fosse win the Best Director Oscar in 1973?

14 Of which movie, based on a Clive Cussler novel, did its producer declare "It would have been cheaper to lower the Atlantic" on commenting on the amount it lost at the box office?

15 What is the name of the real, 20th century, spacecraft found by the crew in the first *Star Trek* movie?

16 Which highly regarded 1941 movie is generally considered to be a criticism of the newspaper tycoon William R Hearst?

QUIZ 31

1. Which cowboy star was said to be "as elegant on a horse as Fred Astaire was on the dance floor"?

2. What make of car was converted into a time machine and driven by Marty McFly in *Back To The Future*?

3. What speed does Marty McFly have to attain in his car in order to go *Back To The Future*?

4. Which British actor played a leading role, Elliot, in the movie *Hannah And Her Sisters*?

5. What type of bomber-plane is *Memphis Belle,* in the World War II movie of the same name?

6. Which famous singer plays the part of Eva Duarte in the movie *Evita*?

7. Which long-serving actor appeared as Spencer Trilby in the movie *True Lies*?

8. Which famous novel by John Steinbeck has been made into movies several times, the earliest being in 1939, starring Lon Chaney Jr and Burgess Meredith?

9 In which 1974 movie does German reporter Peter Miller, played by Jon Voight, follow the trail of Nazi war criminal Eduard Roschmann?

10 Barbra Streisand was the star of which two related movies of 1968 and 1975?

11 *Explorers,* a 1985 science fantasy movie, was the first feature for which actor who died in 1993, aged 23?

12 The British actor Peter Finch won a posthumous Best Actor Oscar for his portrayal of deranged TV presenter Howard Beale, in which movie of 1976?

13 Who was born Roy Harold Scherer Jr in 1925 and died, from AIDS, as one of Hollywood's leading men, in 1985?

14 Then aged five years, which actress made her screen debut as an extra in a famous 1969 movie starring her father, Peter?

15 Who portrayed Kaspar Gutman, aka The Fat Man, in The Maltese Falcon?

16 What was the profession of Clint Eastwood's character in *The Bridges Of Madison County*?

QUIZ 32

1. Who was dubbed 'The Man of a Thousand Faces' during the silent movie era?

2. Who played the lead female role opposite Cary Grant in *North By Northwest*?

3. The drug L-Dopa is the subject of which 1990 movie, starring Robert De Niro and Robin Williams?

4. In *Butch Cassidy And The Sundance Kid,* who was originally set to play Sundance, but dropped out after failing to agree who (he or Paul Newman) was to get top billing?

5. Based on the 1950s TV series, which 1987 movie, directed by Brian De Palma, is set in Prohibition era Chicago?

6. *Along Came A Spider* was the originally intended title of which comedy-horror movie?

7. Bruce Banner changes into which comic-book superhero in a movie released in 2008?

8. 'This is the weekend they didn't play golf' was the tag line to which 1972 adventure drama, starring Jon Voight and Burt Reynolds?

9 Who portrayed Wyatt Earp in the 1993 movie *Tombstone*?

10 *Stagecoach*, the classic 1939 John Wayne western movie, was filmed in which famed Arizona/Utah valley?

11 Which famous movie actress is the daughter of actress Blythe Danner?

12 In which 2000 drama movie does Will Keane (Richard Gere) find it hard to commit to new-found love Charlotte Fielding (Winona Ryder)?

13 In which movie does Daryl Hannah play the role of a mermaid?

14 *The Good Earth,* a 1937 movie adapted from a novel by Pearl S Buck, and starring Paul Muni and Luise Rainer, is set in which country?

15 Which 1941 western movie starred Errol Flynn as General George Custer and Anthony Quinn as Crazy Horse?

16 Which *Tarzan* actor won six Olympic medals during the 1920s?

QUIZ 33

1 Which 1991 episodic movie, starring Winona Ryder, features a soundtrack recorded by Tom Waits?

2 Which James M Cain novel was made into a 1945 movie starring Joan Crawford in the title role, and also featuring Ann Blyth and Zachary Scott?

3 Who played the lead female role, opposite Marlon Brando, in *Last Tango In Paris*?

4 Which star of *The King And I* died on the same day (October 12th 1985) as Orson Welles?

5 Which other star is Rosanna Arquette looking for in *Desperately Seeking Susan,* the movie of 1985?

6 In which Disney comedy movie does Rick Moranis play the role of inventor Wayne Szalinski?

7 What kind of animal was Clyde, Clint Eastwood's pet in *Every Which Way But Loose*?

8 Wallace Beery portrayed which showman and circus founder in a movie of 1934?

9 Which actress, born Jane Alice Peters, has a bridge in her home town of Fort Wayne, Indiana, named after her?

10 *San Francisco,* the 1936 movie about the 1906 earthquake, starred which popular actress of the time?

11 Which 1974 movie, starring Walter Matthau, tells the story of the hijacking of a New York subway train?

12 Michael Caine and Sean Connery star in which 1975 John Huston-directed adventure movie, which was based on a story by Rudyard Kipling?

13 *The Last Valley,* an historical drama movie starring Omar Sharif and Michael Caine is set during which terrible 17th century European war?

14 Who played Marine Sergeant John Stryker in the 1950 movie *Sands Of Iwo Jima*?

15 Which actor played the deranged General Jack D Ripper in *Dr Strangelove*?

16 Who received a Best Actress Oscar in 1990 for her performance in the movie *Misery*?

QUIZ 34

1. Who stars as the saloon singer Frenchy in the classic western *Destry Rides Again*?

2. Which 1994 comedy movie stars Jim Carrey and Jeff Daniels?

3. Which political satire movie of 1972 stars Robert Redford as reluctant politician Bill McKay?

4. Who plays Judge Dredd in the 1995 comic strip-based movie of the same name?

5. *Call Me,* by Blondie, was the intro song to which 1980 movie, starring Richard Gere?

6. Which famous rock singer stars as The Maestro in the 1997 short movie, *Ghosts*?

7. In 1993, which movie corporation purchased Miramax?

8. Which multimedia company was founded in 1994 by Steven Spielberg, David Geffen and Jeffrey Katzenberg?

9 Which 1966 movie, based on a famous novel by Ray Bradbury, tells of a future where all books are outlawed and systematically burned?

10 Who played Walter Matthau's girlfriend in the 1969 comedy movie *Cactus Flower*?

11 *Cleopatra*, the epic movie of 1963, starred which famous 'screen couple' in the title role and the role of Marc Antony?

12 Which 1935 Hitchcock movie, starring Robert Donat, is based on a novel by John Buchan?

13 Who portrayed Captain 'Trapper John' McIntyre in the 1970 movie *M.A.S.H.*?

14 Which celebrated American comedian played the part of Major Major in the World War II movie *Catch 22*?

15 Who portrayed frontman Jim Morrison in the 1991 rock biopic, *The Doors*?

16 What is the name of the spaceman toy in *Toy Story*?

QUIZ 35

1 Which famous British actor/producer/director appeared as the architect of Jurassic Park in the 1993 movie of the same name?

2 Which American comedian, in the part of Smiler Grogan 'dies' near the beginning of *It's A Mad, Mad, Mad, Mad World*?

3 Famous for her Oscar-winning role in *Driving Miss Daisy*, which actress was born in London, England, in 1909?

4 *Return Of The Jedi* is which number episode in the *Star Wars* series?

5 Which epic 1977 World War II movie, about an Allied invasion of Holland, was based on the Cornelius Ryan novel of the same name?

6 In which of the *Lord Of The Rings* trilogy does the mighty Battle of Helm's Deep take place?

7 Which actor and actress headed the cast of *Move Over, Darling,* the hit comedy movie of 1963?

8 *Titanic,* of 1997, featured which Academy Award-winning song?

9 What was the subtitle of *Terminator 2*?

10 "Heeeeere's Johnny!" is a famous line by Jack Nicholson's character in which movie?

11 Which actress was Oscar-nominated for her role as ageing movie star Norma Desmond in *Sunset Boulevard,* of 1950?

12 Which *Baywatch* star plays the part of Becca in the third *Scary Movie*?

13 Who is the assassination target of The Jackal, played by Bruce Willis, in the 1997 movie of the same name?

14 *The Osterman Weekend* was the last movie to be directed by which sometimes controversial director?

15 Who portrayed the Vulcan, Lieutenant Saavik, in *Star Trek II*?

16 In 1919, which famous actor from the silent movie era lost a finger and thumb from his right hand during the making of the movie *Haunted Spooks*?

QUIZ 36

1. Which 1994 movie, starring Harrison Ford as Jack Ryan, is based on a novel of the same name by Tom Clancy?

2. In which year was the sequel to Disney's 1940 *Fantasia* released?

3. In which Woody Allen movie does health-food shop owner, Miles Monroe, go into hospital for a routine operation and wake up 200 years later?

4. Who won the 1964 Best Director Oscar for *My Fair Lady*?

5. Mel Gibson and Danny Glover play a couple of Los Angeles detectives in which series of 1980s/90s movies?

6. Robert Redford and others founded which (appropriately titled) movie festival which takes place in Utah every year?

7. Portraying the character 'Swede' Anderson, whose movie debut was in the 1946 movie *The Killers*?

8. Which movie actress' three marriages were to Mickey Rooney, Frank Sinatra and Artie Shaw?

9 Who played the part of paranoid surveillance expert Harry Caul, in *The Conversation*, a 1974 movie directed by Francis Ford Coppola?

10 What is the title of the second sequel to the 1981 horror movie *The Evil Dead*?

11 Atop which New York skyscraper did the final action of *King Kong* (1933 original, and the second remake of 2005), take place?

12 Which 1969 movie about a Depression-era dance marathon starred Jane Fonda in the part of Gloria?

13 The action in the 1988 movie *Dangerous Liaisons,* starring John Malkovich and Glenn Close, takes place in which country?

14 Who was the presenter who ad-libbed his way out of an awkward situation when the 1974 Academy Awards ceremony was disrupted by a streaker?

15 The stop-motion techniques of Nick Park and Aardman Animations have produced several animated movies featuring which fun duo?

16 Who played the lead female role opposite Gregory Peck in the 1945 Hitchcock movie *Spellbound*?

QUIZ 37

1. After being dropped by MGM in 1950, in which 1954 Warner Brothers musical movie did Judy Garland make a spectacular comeback to the silver screen?

2. Which actor's first big movie appearance was in *One Million BC* (1940) and his last in *Firepower* (1979)?

3. Which actor of short stature, who starred in many movies from the 1930s to 1964, is probably best remembered for his starring role in *Shane,* of 1953?

4. Which actor, famous for his fast living, who died aged 50 in 1959, is said to be buried with six bottles of his favorite whiskey in his coffin?

5. The 1998 American remake of *Godzilla* starred which actor in the lead role of Dr Nick Tatopoulos?

6. Which star of *St Elmo's Fire* appeared as TV executive Benjamin Kane in *Wayne's World*?

7. Whoopi Goldberg, Danny Glover and Oprah Winfrey all appeared in which Spielberg movie of 1985?

8. What is the name of the 'American president' who climbs aboard a fighter-plane to combat the aliens in *Independence Day*?

9 The 1944 comedy movie *Miracle Of Morgan's Creek* starred which singer/actress in the part of Trudy Kockenlocker?

10 Charles Bronson, under his real name of Charles Buchinsky, appeared as Vincent Price's assistant, Igor, in which 1953 classic horror movie?

11 *The Magnificent Seven,* the classic 1960 Western, was a re-working and re-setting of which Japanese movie of 1954?

12 Which actor, famous as Ilya Kuryakin in TV's *The Man From U.N.C.L.E.*, appeared in the 1980 thriller *The Watcher In The Woods*?

13 Which Spielberg 1985 movie was rereleased in 2002 with new special effects and extra scenes?

14 The 1991 comedy movie *City Slickers* starred which actor in the role of Mitch Robbins?

15 Who starred as Long John Silver in the 1990 version of *Treasure Island*?

16 Which famous tough-guy movie actor was born Volodymyr Palahnuik in 1919?

QUIZ 38

1. Which 1999 comedy movie is about the worn-out cast of a *Star Trek*-like fictional TV series?

2. Which 1999 movie, starring Tom Hanks, is mostly set in the environs of 'Cold Mountain Penitentiary'?

3. Who plays the female lead opposite Colin Farrell in the 2006 movie *Ask The Dust*?

4. Tobey Maguire starred as Homer Wells in which 1999 drama movie set, at the outset, in an orphanage?

5. Which multi-award winning movie of 2000 tells the story of Vianne Rocher, played by Juliette Binoche, and a candy store in a French village?

6. Which 2001 movie, starring Kevin Spacey and Julianne Moore, is set in the fictional town of Quoyle Point on the coast of Newfoundland?

7. Who played the part of Lois Lane in the *Superman* (1978-1987) movies?

8. Who played the part of Lex Luthor in the *Superman* movies?

9 Which 1997 horror movie had amongst the cast a certain actress from TV's *Buffy The Vampire Slayer*?

10 *Gallipoli,* the 1981 movie which helped launch Mel Gibson's career, was a fictional account of a real battle that took place in which war?

11 Rock Hudson played a Navy commander, Ernest Borgnine a Russian defector, and Patrick McGoohan a British agent in which action movie of 1968?

12 The World War II action movie *Where Eagles Dare* starred which American actor in the role of Lt. Morris Schaffer?

13 Which actor/singer starred in movie musicals such as *Annie Get Your Gun, Showboat* and *Calamity Jane,* before eventually appearing as Clayton Farlow in TV's *Dallas*?

14 The *Mad Max* movie series, which portrays a bleak and violent future, is set in which country?

15 The action in the hard-hitting movie *Midnight Express* takes place in a prison in which country?

16 Who played the lead female role in *My Best Friend's Wedding,* a romantic comedy movie of 1997?

QUIZ 39

1. The book *The Devil's Candy* is about the making of which movie?

2. Which 1991 movie, starring Matt Dillon and Sean Young, is based on a famous novel by Ira Levin?

3. 'It's hotter than hell' was the tagline for which 1997 disaster movie?

4. Which actor played the Scarecrow in *The Wizard Of Oz*?

5. Despite being nominated for eleven Oscars, which 1977 movie, starring Shirley MacLaine and Anne Bancroft, won not even one?

6. In 2004, which 2003 movie won all of the eleven Oscars for which it was nominated?

7. Which baseball ace did John Goodman portray in a biopic of 1992?

8. Which Oscar-winning 2005 drama movie tells the story of two cowboys, portrayed by Heath Ledger and Jake Gyllenhaal?

9 In which 1998 movie are Reese Witherspoon and Tobey Maguire given a TV remote control that takes them into a monochrome 1950s 'TV world' version of their lives?

10 Which actress played the part of Betty Rizzo in *Grease* and the wife in *Meet The Applegates*?

11 Kirk Douglas played the title role in which Stanley Kubrick-directed movie of 1960?

12 James Caan and his real-life son, Scott, starred as a father and son in which 1995 movie?

13 Who does shy, introverted Stanley Ipkiss, played by Jim Carrey, turn into in a 1994 comic book-based movie?

14 Which violent 1994 movie, directed by Oliver Stone, starring Woody Harrelson and Juliette Lewis, had to be substantially cut to get past censors in America?

15 Which 2004 environmental-catastrophe movie, despite being flawed by the impossible climate-change scenario that it presented, proved to be one of the highest earning movies of all time?

16 Which town features in the movie *Groundhog Day?*

QUIZ 40

1. Nora Ephron's marriage to Carl Bernstein is the basis for the story in which movie starring Meryl Streep and Jack Nicholson?

2. Who plays the unnamed American photo-journalist in *Apocalypse Now*?

3. Which future politician starred opposite Barbara Stanwyck in the 1954 western *Cattle Queen Of Montana*?

4. Phileas Fogg, played by David Niven, is the main character in which 1956 movie, based on a novel by Jules Verne?

5. Starring Burt Lancaster and Dean Martin, which 1970 movie, based on a novel by Arthur Hailey, was one of the very first 'disaster movies'?

6. What was Marlene Dietrich's last movie?

7. Whose song *Streets Of Philadelphia* received an Oscar for its appearance in the 1993 movie *Philadelphia*?

8. What is the new 'cyborg' name of murdered police officer Alex J Murphy in a 1987 action movie?

9 In which 1992 movie does Sean Connery discover a cure for cancer in the Amazon rainforest, only to have it destroyed by loggers and a forest fire?

10 In *Forrest Gump,* Peter Dobson plays the part, and Kurt Russell does the voice, of which singer?

11 Which 1991 Steven Spielberg-directed movie is based on J M Barrie's *Peter Pan*?

12 Starring Jane Fonda and Michael Douglas, which 1979 movie relates the story of a news reporter's discovery of safety cover-ups at a nuclear plant?

13 Who starred as Chili Palmer in *Get Shorty*?

14 How are Michelle Pfeiffer, Cher and Susan Sarandon collectively known in a movie of 1987?

15 Which British comic actor appeared as songwriter George Webber in the movie *10*?

16 What was the highest gross-earning movie of the 1990s?

QUIZ 41

1. In *The Lion King*, what is the name of the cub who grows up to become the king of the Lions?

2. In which African country does Sigourney Weaver, as the naturalist Dian Fossey, have her encounters with the *Gorillas In The Mist*?

3. Who played the role of Ann Darrow, the heroine, in the first *King Kong* movie?

4. Who is the small 'brother' of Arnold Schwarzenegger in the movie *Twins*?

5. Which actor played opposite Elizabeth Taylor in *National Velvet*?

6. Which 1998 Tom Hanks/Meg Ryan movie was a remake of the 1940 movie *The Shop Around The Corner*?

7. Which composer wrote the music for the 1949 movie *On The Town*?

8. Who was satirized in the 1940 Charlie Chaplin movie *The Great Dictator*?

9 'Love means never having to say you're sorry' is the tagline to which 1970 movie?

10 Who won an Oscar for her role as Irene Hoffman Wallner in the 1961 movie *Judgment At Nuremburg*?

11 In 1985, Jack Nicholson and Kathleen Turner starred as a 'hit man' and 'hit girl' in which movie?

12 According to Forrest Gump, "Life is like a ..." what?

13 In *Schindler's List*, what is Schindler's first name?

14 Who received a Best Actress Oscar for her role as Nurse Mildred Ratched in *One Flew Over The Cuckoo's Nest*?

15 The 1945 movie *A Royal Scandal* starred Tallulah Bankhead as which famous Russian empress?

16 Who played Clark Griswold in the *National Lampoon* movies of the 1980s?

QUIZ 42

1. Who played the married couple who were unfaithful to each other in 1991's *Scenes From A Mall*?

2. Which 1982 Francis Ford Coppola movie, starring Frederic Forrest and Teri Garr, is set entirely in Las Vegas?

3. Whose first movie role was Joan Vecchio in the 1970 movie *Lovers And Other Strangers*?

4. Which novel by Michael Crichton, about an accidentally-released man-made organism, was turned into a 1971 movie and a 2008 TV mini-series?

5. Originally intended to have the title *$3000*, under what title did this 1990 movie eventually appear?

6. Which veteran actor appears as the character *Number 2* in the Austin Powers movies?

7. Active in movies since 1948, which actress made a cameo appearance – as herself – in the 2004 movie *Connie And Carla*?

8. In which year did Disney's first full-length animated movie, *Snow White And The Seven Dwarfs*, appear?

9 Who played the part of Khan in *Star Trek II: The Wrath Of Khan*?

10 *Kiss Of Death* (1947) was the first movie role – as the hoodlum Tommy Udo – for which actor, who died in 2008, aged 93?

11 The famous 'rolling in the surf' sequence in *From Here To Eternity* was performed by which actor and actress?

12 Which infamous real-life Nazi doctor was portrayed by Gregory Peck in *The Boys From Brazil*?

13 Which hero of English legend fights the monster, Grendel, in a 2007 'sword and sandal' movie?

14 In Disney's 1992 *Aladdin*, who provides the voice parts of the Genie and the lamp-selling Peddler?

15 Which *Ally McBeal* star appeared as Helena in the 1999 movie adaptation of William Shakespeare's *A Midsummer Night's Dream*?

16 Perhaps best known for his role in TV's *Starsky And Hutch*, who appeared as Perchik in the 1971 movie version of *Fiddler On The Roof*?

QUIZ 43

1. Who plays the role of Marshal Samuel Gerard in the 1993 movie *The Fugitive*?

2. Which rock star appeared with Emilio Estevez and Rene Russo in the science fiction movie *Freejack*?

3. What, according to the 1994 movie's tagline, 'will take you a million light-years from home – but will it bring you back?'

4. 'You will hear what you see', a statement on the poster for the 1929 movie *In Old Arizona*, referred to what unique factor?

5. Which silent-movie era actor was nicknamed 'The Great Stone Face'?

6. What is the title of the 2003 sequel to the 2001 movie *Atlantis: The Lost Empire*?

7. Which TV's *Happy Days* actor starred with Sally Field in the 1977 comedy-drama movie *Heroes*?

8. Which Vietnam War-based movie ends with the American troops singing the 'Mickey Mouse Club' song as they march through the ruins of a town?

9 Which Dustin Hoffman/Meryl Streep movie won five Oscars in 1979?

10 Who had to decline the offer to play the part of Indiana Jones when he decided to stay with his contract to star in TV's *Magnum P.I.*?

11 Carol Anne Freeling, aged five, encounters malevolent spirits via static on a TV screen in which 1982 horror movie?

12 Which 1960 movie, based on a novel by Leon Uris, portrays Holocaust survivors who are stranded on a ship, attempting to get to Israel?

13 Which 1946 movie, starring Lana Turner and John Garfield, was remade in 1981, with Jack Nicholson and Jessica Lange in the lead roles?

14 Which comedy crew stow away on a ship bound for America in the 1931 movie, *Monkey Business*?

15 The life of which spiritual leader is the subject of the Martin Scorsese-directed movie *Kundun*?

16 Which 1987 movie, starring Ryan O'Neal and Isabella Rossellini, was written and directed by Norman Mailer?

QUIZ 44

1. What was the title of the 1988 sequel to the 1985 movie *Cocoon*?

2. In which 1993 movie does Sandra Bullock disappear in a gas station, much to the consternation of her 'boyfriend', Kiefer Sutherland?

3. In *Forrest Gump*, which three US presidents does Tom Hanks 'meet'?

4. Which movie family's ancient car made an appearance at the 2008 New York Auto Show?

5. The name of a Swiss mountain appears in the title of which Clint Eastwood movie?

6. Which 2003 comedy movie, starring Steve Martin, is about a chaotic family with twelve children?

7. Which Disney movie, with a Halloween theme, stars Bette Midler and Sarah Jessica Parker?

8. In which 1988 comedy movie does Michael Caine teach his con artist talents to Steve Martin?

9 Who played the two main characters, half-brothers Einar and Eric, in the 1958 epic movie *The Vikings*?

10 Who 'discovered herself' after the death of her husband in a 1999 movie starring Anjelica Huston?

11 Which actress received a Best Supporting Actress Oscar for her role in *The Diary Of Anne Frank,* the autobiographical movie released in 1959?

12 Who played the part of Clark Kent's father in *Superman: The Movie* (1978)?

13 Ethan Hawke portrayed Nando Parrado in which 1993 disaster/survival movie, based on an actual event that happened in 1972?

14 The events of September 11th 2001 are the basis of which 2006 movie, directed by Oliver Stone?

15 In which 1957 romantic movie do Cary Grant and Deborah Kerr arrange to meet atop the Empire State Building in six months if they each want to continue their affair?

16 Which couple starred in the 1949 classic comedy *Adam's Rib*?

QUIZ 45

1. Which 1957 Kubrick movie, starring Kirk Douglas, was based on a novel by Humphrey Cobb, about events in the French army during World War I?

2. Which 1981 movie, based on the King Arthur legend, starred Nigel Terry and Helen Mirren?

3. The vocal quartet The Four Aces had a No 1 hit in 1954 with which Academy Award-winning song from the movie of the same name?

4. Humphrey Bogart's relationship with Lauren Bacall started during the shooting of which movie?

5. Who played the part of Jack Swigert in *Apollo 13*?

6. Which 1981 horror movie, starring Kurt Russell, is set on an Antarctic base that is occupied by a morphing alien being?

7. Who played the part of the demon-possessed young girl, Regan MacNeil, in the *Exorcist*?

8. Which Redford/Pfeiffer 1996 romantic movie is a story based on the career of a TV anchorwoman?

9 Sales of clown fish rose dramatically after the release of which 2003 Disney animated movie?

10 Which 1990 movie, starring Gabriel Byrne, is about a power struggle between gang bosses Liam O'Bannon and Johnny Caspar?

11 The stories within which 2003 movie are told by a hospitalized detective novelist, Dan Dark, played by Robert Downey Jr?

12 Who directed the Oscar-winning 1974 movie *Chinatown*?

13 In *Gone With The Wind*, what is Rhett Butler's famous reply to Scarlett's question: "Rhett, if you go, where shall I go, what shall I do?"?

14 Which 1962 political thriller movie, staring Frank Sinatra, was remade in 2004, starring Denzel Washington?

15 The Oscar-winning song *Secret Love* comes from which movie, starring Doris Day in the title role?

16 The songs *Wand'rin' Star* and *I Talk To The Trees* are featured in which 1969 musical movie?

QUIZ 46

1 'Six reasons the West was wild' is the tagline of which 1988 western movie, starring Emilio Estevez and Kiefer Sutherland?

2 *The Alamo* movie of 2004 starred which actor in the part of Davy Crockett?

3 *The Alamo* movie of 1960 starred which actor in the part of Davy Crockett?

4 Which movie-making duo directed the 2000 comedy movie, *O Brother, Where Art Thou*?

5 What are the better known names of Jason Derris and Robert Blutarsky, the fictional duo who have appeared in several movies?

6 'The fastest hands in the East meet the biggest mouth in the West' is a tag line from which 1998 martial arts movie starring Jackie Chan?

7 Which 1971 cult movie tells of the relationship between a 79-year-old woman and a young man who likes to stage his own mock suicides?

8 Who played the main female role opposite Jack Nicholson in *Five Easy Pieces*?

9 Which Swedish actor played the part of Father Lankester Merrin in *The Exorcist*?

10 The actor William Boyd is best remembered for his numerous performances as which cowboy hero?

11 Which famous musical brothers wrote the songs for the 1957 movie *Funny Face*?

12 The tagline went: 'Nothing's going to hold you like Hitchcock's …' what? (The title of the 1948 movie, starring James Stewart).

13 Which rabbit is the invisible companion of Elwood P Dowd in a famous 1950 movie?

14 Which Canadian-born actor played Abraham Lincoln in the 1962 movie *How The West Was Won?*

15 Which comedian played the straight role of crooked building developer Arnold Ross in the 1989 comedy movie *Cookie*?

16 The 'Hotel New Hampshire' – the title of the 1984 movie, starring Jodie Foster and Rob Lowe – was situated in which European city?

QUIZ 47

1 Which famous comedy actor was born Arthur Stanley Jefferson, in Ulverston, England, in 1890?

2 Who appeared in the TV soap opera *Another World* before making his movie debut in *Who Says I Can't Ride A Rainbow*, a movie from 1971?

3 The songs *America*, *Tonight* and *Maria* all appear in which musical movie?

4 For his portrayal of which comedian was Dustin Hoffman nominated for Best Actor Oscar in 1974?

5 Which classic 1935 sea-based movie, starring Charles Laughton and Clark Gable, was nominated for eight Oscars, but won only one, for Best Picture?

6 *The Jewel Of The Nile* is the sequel to which adventure movie of 1984?

7 Bruce Willis saves planet Earth from total destruction by a giant asteroid in which 1998 movie?

8 Comedian Joe E Lewis, portrayed by Frank Sinatra, is the subject of which biopic of 1957?

9 Starring Steve Martin, which 1987 movie is based on the play *Cyrano de Bergerac*?

10 In the 1991 spoof movie, *Hot Shots*, which former Middle East dictator gets a surprise when, relaxing by his pool, a large bomb lands in his lap?

11 At the very end of *Schindler's List,* who places flowers on the grave of the real Oskar Schindler?

12 Who played the main guys in the 1955 musical movie *Guys And Dolls*?

13 Which British actress appears as the nurse Evelyn Johnson in the 2001 movie *Pearl Harbor*?

14 What was the title of the American-Japanese 1970 movie that was based on the 1941 attack on Pearl Harbor?

15 In 2003, which American politician made a cameo appearance, as himself, in *Anger Management*?

16 *Cold Mountain* and *The Talented Mr Ripley* are movies made by which British director, who died in 2008?

QUIZ 48

1. *A Wink And A Smile*, is an Oscar-nominated song that featured in which 1993 movie?

2. *A Slight Case Of Murder*, a black comedy classic of 1938, starred which esteemed movie gangster?

3. *Man Of La Mancha*, a movie of 1972 starring Peter O'Toole, has its origins in which classic novel?

4. Little Richard's song *Great Gosh A'mighty* made a very successful appearance in which 1986 movie, starring Nick Nolte, Richard Dreyfuss and Bette Midler?

5. Which literary-based movie of 1940 tells of the Joad family's tribulations during the 1930s Great Depression?

6. Singer Pat Boone made a rare big-screen appearance in which adventure movie of 1959?

7. Which variation on the 'Cinderella' theme brought a 1998 movie starring Drew Barrymore and Anjelica Huston?

8. Which notoriously violent martial arts-themed Tarantino movies (2003 and 2004), star Uma Thurman in the role of Beatrix Kiddo?

9 Who played John Wayne's 'wife' in the 1963 comedy Western *McLintock!*?

10 Who won the 1953 Best Actress Oscar for her performance in *Roman Holiday*?

11 In which 1968 movie does a private eye (played by Frank Sinatra) find a dead blonde on his morning swim?

12 Which blockbuster won Best Picture Oscar in 2000?

13 "T'aint a fit night out for man nor beast" is uttered by which snow-bound comedian in *The Fatal Glass Of Beer*, a comedy movie of 1933?

14 Dustin Hoffman received an Oscar nomination for his role in which 1997 movie about a conspiracy to divert attention away from the President's misbehavior?

15 Which movie, about a dog that is half-wolf, is based on the Jack London novel of the same name?

16 Which long-running, highly successful science fiction TV series found its way into the movie theatre for the second time in 2008 – the first time being in 1998?

QUIZ 49

1. Which Orson Welles-produced and directed movie of 1942 was based on the novel of the same title by Booth Tarkington?

2. In which city does Judy Garland invite you to meet her, in a 1944 movie?

3. Lt Pete 'Maverick' Mitchell and Lt Nick 'Goose' Bradshaw team up in which 1986 movie?

4. Which super-villain was played by Jim Carrey in *Batman Forever*?

5. In which movie, set in a crime-ridden future America, is Snake Plissken given just 24 hours to find the kidnapped US President?

6. What was the sub-title of *Police Academy 7*?

7. Which movie, based on a long-running crime drama TV series, requested 'Just the facts' in its tagline?

8. Starring Kathleen Turner in the title role, which movie tells of a woman, on the brink of divorce, reliving her younger life, at a 25th high school reunion?

9 Which 2004 Coen brothers movie, about a criminal gang who are single-handedly defeated by an old lady, is a remake of a 1955 British movie with the same title?

10 In whch movie does Clint Eastwood star in the role of disc jockey Dave Garver?

11 What does Pee-wee lose, and go looking for, in *Pee-wee's Big Adventure*?

12 Which 1990 movie stars Tom Hanks as Joe Banks?

13 Jack Crabb, who claimed to be 121 years old, was known to the native Americans who raised him as whom (also the 1970 movie's title)?

14 What is the name of the snake character in Disney's 1973 animated movie, *Robin Hood*?

15 Which 1980 movie marked the directorial debut of Robert Redford, and earned him an Oscar in the process?

16 After *Pretty Woman,* what was the next movie to star Richard Gere and Julia Roberts?

QUIZ 50

1. Which character is the chief villain in the *Austin Powers* series of movies?

2. Who is the famous 'son' of 'Professor Henry Jones'?

3. Which 1998 romantic comedy movie starred Ben Stiller, Cameron Diaz and Matt Dillon?

4. What is Wesley Snipes' character's job in the movie *Passenger 57*?

5. 'Something happens when she hears the music' and 'What a feeling!' are taglines to which movie, starring Jennifer Beals?

6. In which Biblical epic of 1965 does John Wayne make a fleeting cameo appearance with the line, "Truly, this man is the son of God"?

7. Which pair wrote, produced and directed the Oscar-winning 1996 black comedy movie *Fargo*?

8. What is the name of the panda hero of the 2008 animated movie *Kung Fu Panda*?

9 What was the title of the sequel to *Three Men And A Baby*?

10 The movie *La Bamba* is a 1987 biopic of which pop singer?

11 Which movie had the tagline 'In Vietnam the wind doesn't blow, it sucks'?

12 Who plays Steve Martin's unfaithful wife in the movie, *The Man With Two Brains?*

13 Which actor's scenes were completely edited out of the 1983 movie *The Big Chill*?

14 Charlton Heston as Moses, Yul Brynner as Pharaoh Rameses II: which 1956 DeMille-directed Biblical epic?

15 Which 1995 movie told of a hotel bellhop's various experiences during one New Year's Eve?

16 Which British actor starred in, and part-produced, the 2007 movie *Sleuth*?

QUIZ 51

1 Which 2002 movie, about a young soldier's perceived cowardice, was the second remake; the previous movies appearing in 1929 and 1939?

2 Who played the wife of Jim Garrison (played by Kevin Costner) in the movie *JFK*?

3 Who plays Leo Biederman, the amateur astronomer who alerts the authorities to an incoming comet which will destroy planet Earth, in *Deep Impact*?

4 The 1989 Steven Spielberg movie *Always,* included the final big-screen appearance of which celebrated actress?

5 John Rhys-Davies played the part of the archaeologist Sallah in the *Indiana Jones* movies. Which part did he play in the *Lord Of The Rings* trilogy?

6 Which rock star played the part of Tiny in *Wayne's World*?

7 At the end of which movie does Groucho Marx say to Margaret Dumont "Marry me Emily, and I'll never look at another horse"?

8 What was the sub-title of *Star Trek III*?

9 Lauren Bacall and Marilyn Monroe were two members of the gold-digging trio in *How To Marry a Millionaire;* who was the third?

10 Which Marvel Comics superhero-based movie, starring Robert Downey Jr, was released in 2008?

11 Which actor, who starred in the 1950s/60s TV underwater-themed series *Sea Hunt,* appeared in *Airplane!*?

12 Based on the Scott Smith novel of the same title, which movie tells of the events following the discovery of a hoard of cash on a crashed plane?

13 *The Power Of Love* is the title of a 1922 movie that was the first to use which novel visual technique?

14 Who played the role of cocaine-dealing gangster Tony Montana in the 1983 movie *Scarface*?

15 In *Robin Hood: Prince Of Thieves*, which part is played by Mary Elizabeth Mastrantonio?

16 After *Platoon* and *Born On The Fourth Of July,* what is the third Oliver Stone movie with a Vietnam War theme?

QUIZ 52

1. Wesley Snipes and Woody Harrelson both had their big-screen debuts in which football-theme movie of 1986?

2. *The Return Of Captain Invincible*, starred which actor in the title role?

3. How many Oscars were picked up for *Dances With Wolves*?

4. Who portrayed Jerry Lee Lewis in the movie *Great Balls Of Fire*?

5. Who portrayed Jesus of Nazareth in *The Passion Of The Christ*?

6. In *Thelma And Louise*, what innocent pastime are the girls on their way to before things begin to go wrong?

7. What is the name of the Berlin nightclub where Sally Bowles (Liza Minnelli) dances in the movie, *Cabaret*?

8. Spencer Tracy and Mickey Rooney starred in which 1938 movie about a home for delinquent boys?

9 In which 1951 movie is an alien named Klaatu played by Michael Rennie, and in the 2008 remake played by Keanu Reeves?

10 In the original *Jaws* movie, what is the occupation of Quint, the character played by Robert Shaw?

11 Which famous singer played the part of Selina Rogers in the 1943 musical movie *Stormy Weather*?

12 In the movie *Angel Heart,* Robert De Niro plays the part of Louis Cyphre. Which devilish being – as suggested by his name – does Louis Cyphre turn out to be?

13 Which son of Bruce Lee was accidentally shot and killed in the studio during the making of the movie *The Crow*?

14 In which 1965 movie does Frank Sinatra and a group of POWs escape captivity by stealing a train?

15 Which 1978 movie starred Mae West, together with a host of music stars including Alice Cooper and Ringo Starr?

16 Which 1991 drama movie concerns an ascent of the world's second-highest mountain?

QUIZ 53

1 Austin O'Brien plays the part of youngster Danny Madigan, in which Arnold Schwarzenegger 1993 movie?

2 In which movie do you encounter 'Z', the only non-conformist insect in a whole colony, which is situated somewhere in New York's Central Park?

3 Who starred as the mummy in the original (1932) movie of that name?

4 The song *For All We Know* won an Oscar for which 1970 movie?

5 Rita Hayworth as chorus girl Rusty, and Gene Kelly as her boyfriend Danny, starred in which Oscar-winning movie of 1944?

6 The movies *Pillow Talk, Lover Come Back* and *Send Me No Flowers* all starred which male and female duo?

7 Which actor starred opposite Elizabeth Taylor in *Cat On A Hot Tin Roof*?

8 Which 2000 movie starred Ellen Burstyn and Jared Leto as a mother and son who both have a drugs problem?

9 *Morocco*, of 1930, was the American movie debut for which female star?

10 Starring Jean-Claude van Damme, which movie is about a gang who take the US Vice President hostage at a hockey game?

11 Which prolific movie composer wrote scores for *The Naked And The Dead, Psycho* and *Taxi Driver*?

12 In which Hitchcock thriller does Julie Andrews follow her rocket-scientist fiancé, Paul Newman, to East Germany, believing he is about to defect?

13 Who played Arnold Schwarzenegger's wife in *Total Recall*?

14 Which actress, a former wife of Andre Agassi, starred in *The Blue Lagoon*?

15 Which actor made his big-screen debut as a rebellious teenager in the 1979 movie *Over The Edge*?

16 Which movie, based on the novel of the same name by Kurt Vonnegut, tells of Billy Pilgrim and his space/time imaginary journeys?

QUIZ 54

1. Which famous movie star preferred 'Duke' to 'Marion'?

2. In which 1974 Roman Polanski movie does Polanski himself make a cameo appearance as a vicious knifeman?

3. How many times has actress Zsa Zsa Gabor been married?

4. Which 1967 movie, starring Tony Curtis and Claudia Cardinale, was the debut movie of Sharon Tate?

5. In which 1984 movie does a young man start to have problems when he accepts a small creature named Gizmo?

6. Which actress had star roles in *Soldier Blue, Carnal Knowledge* and *Oliver's Story*?

7. *All That Jazz* was a 1979 movie by, and based on the life and work, of which famous choreographer?

8. Which 1975 movie, based on a Raymond Chandler novel of the same title, starred Robert Mitchum in the role of private detective Philip Marlowe?

9 A 1948 3-cent postage stamp bore the image of which silent-movie star, who died, along with the famous aviator Wiley Post, in an airplane crash in 1935?

10 In *Wayne's World,* who is Wayne's studio co-host?

11 In which movie, starring Johnny Depp, can you see a strange tree, named the 'Tree of the Dead'?

12 What is the name of Jodie Foster's character in *Silence Of The Lambs*?

13 Who played the female lead in the original *Smokey And The Bandit* movie?

14 In which movie does Demi Moore play the part of Lt Jordan O'Neill?

15 On the poster for which movie does Demi Moore appear without clothes?

16 Who directed both the Newman/Redford movies, *The Sting* and *Butch Cassidy And The Sundance Kid*?

QUIZ 55

1. Who played the rival bounty hunter Colonel Douglas Mortimer in *For A Few Dollars More*?

2. Who was known as 'The Singing Cowboy'?

3. Which role was played by Leonardo DiCaprio in *The Man In The Iron Mask* (1998)?

4. 'She knew his face, his touch, his voice, she knew everything about him ...but the truth' is the tagline of which post-Civil War movie of 1993?

5. For her role in which 1974 movie did Ellen Burstyn win a Best Actress Oscar?

6. Who played the part of Karen Silkwood in *Silkwood,* a conspiracy theory-based movie of 1983?

7. What was the title of the 1999 sequel to the 1976 horror movie *Carrie*?

8. Which 1996 movie with a sports management theme starred Tom Cruise, Renée Zellweger and Cuba Gooding Jr?

9 In which movie does Robert De Niro play the character Travis Bickle, an insomniac who prefers night-time work?

10 Which 1990 movie, starring Jeremy Irons and Glenn Close, relates the basically true story of an alleged attempted murder within a family called von Bülow?

11 Which 1955 movie, starring Ernest Borgnine as a lonely man with low self-esteem, won four Oscars, including Best Picture and Best Actor?

12 The plot of which 1995 western movie follows the fortunes of four former 'working girls', on the run from a murder charge?

13 Which German airship was the subject, and the title, of a 1975 disaster movie, starring George C Scott?

14 Sean Penn and Bruce Willis appear, as themselves, in which 2008 satirical comedy movie?

15 Who appears as Superman's mother in the *Superman* movies of the 1970s and 1980s?

16 Which British-born musician conducted the Philadelphia Orchestra in Disney's original *Fantasia?*

QUIZ 56

1. Orison Whipple Hungerford III is the real name of which actor, probably most famous as Bronco Layne in the 1950s TV series?

2. What was the substance with miraculous qualities, discovered by Fred MacMurray's character, in *The Absent-Minded Professor*?

3. Which actress lost a multi-million dollar lawsuit as a result of her withdrawal from the movie *Boxing Helena*?

4. In the 1957 movie *The Prince And The Showgirl*, Marilyn Monroe was the showgirl; which British actor was the prince?

5. Which actor and comedian was born David Daniel Kaminsky?

6. Which science fiction movie tells the story of '5', a 'Sandman' – an official executioner who deals out death on the thirtieth birthday of each person on the planet?

7. In the 2005 movie, who played *Mr & Mrs Smith*?

8. Which comedy actor starred as the robot in *Bicentennial Man?*

9 Which 1965 movie, the last for Vivien Leigh, tells the stories of certain individuals on a 1930s cruise ship?

10 What dish was the speciality of the Whistle Stop Cafe, in a 1991 movie based on a novel by Fannie Flagg?

11 Which 1973 Jack Lemmon movie had the tagline 'Juggle the books. Set fire to the factory. Supply women for the clients. Harry Stoner will do anything to get one more season'?

12 Who plays the female lead character, restaurant-owner, Jo Ann, in *Tequila Sunrise* of 1988?

13 Which real-life brothers starred in *The Fabulous Baker Boys*?

14 Humphrey Bogart starred as Frank McCloud and Lauren Bacall as Nora Temple in which 1948 movie?

15 The 1994 movie *Love Affair*, starring Warren Beatty, saw the last appearance of which celebrated actress who died in 2003?

16 Which actress directed and starred in the 1991 movie *Prince Of Tides*?

QUIZ 57

1. Which rock idol starred as The Kid in the movie *Purple Rain*?

2. Which movie of 1963, starring Charlton Heston and Ava Gardner, is set in the time of the 1900 Boxer uprising in China?

3. Which 2001 World War II movie's plot tells of two snipers – one German, the other Russian – as they stalk each other through the ruins of Stalingrad?

4. *Flags Of Our Fathers* is a 2006 Clint Eastwood-directed movie about the World War II battle for which Pacific island?

5. Which 1963 comedy movie, starring Jerry Lewis, was remade in 1996, this time with Eddie Murphy?

6. What is the name of the small boy accidentally left at home in *Home Alone*?

7. Which city features in the title of the second *Home Alone* movie?

8. In *My Fair Lady*, what is the name of the character played by Audrey Hepburn?

9 'Life is a terrible thing to sleep through' is a tagline to which 1993 movie, starring Johnny Depp?

10 Which big-screen movie was the last to star Christopher Reeve, before his career was cut short by a riding accident?

11 Which *Star Wars* actress was once the step-daughter of Elizabeth Taylor?

12 Her performance in the 1993 movie *Born Yesterday* earned which actress a Golden Raspberry Award nomination?

13 What is Rambo's first name?

14 Who played the role of Willy Wonka in *Willy Wonka And The Chocolate Factory*?

15 The movie *Amadeus* was a biopic on the life of which Austrian composer?

16 Which song-and-dance man appeared with Olivia Newton-John in the 1980 movie *Xanadu*?

QUIZ 58

1. Walt Disney died during the production of which animated feature movie, released in 1967?

2. What is the subtitle of the 2008 movie *The Mummy*?

3. Which 1964 movie, starring Lee Marvin and Angie Dickinson, was the only one in which Ronald Reagan appeared as a 'bad guy' ?

4. *Kiss Me Deadly* (1955) and *The Girl Hunters* (1963) both featured which Mickey Spillane-created detective?

5. Which 2000 movie, starring Michael Douglas, tells four different stories about the effects of illegal drugs; from the point-of-view of a trafficker, a user, a law-enforcer and a politician?

6. Which father and son appeared in the 1987 movie *Wall Street*?

7. Starring Kathy Bates and Jennifer Jason Leigh, *Dolores Claiborne* is a 1995 movie based on the novel of the same title, by which author?

8. Who directed *The Wid Bunch,* a movie of 1969?

9 Who starred as The Driver, in the 1978 movie of the same name?

10 Who or what is Event Horizon, in the 1997 science fiction movie of the same name?

11 In which movie does Robin Williams portray disc jockey Adrian Cronauer?

12 Which actress, who played the unfaithful wife in *What's Eating Gilbert Grape*, married actor Ted Danson in 1995?

13 Which Mrs Spielberg appeared in *Indiana Jones And The Temple Of Doom*?

14 Susan Hayward starred in which 1955 biopic about the life of Broadway star Lillian Roth?

15 Which 1983 Francis Ford Coppola teen-angst movie featured the characters Ponyboy, Sodapop and Two-Bit?

16 Clint Eastwood produced, directed and starred in which war movie of 1986?

QUIZ 59

1. What was the year of release of the epic movie *How The West Was Won*?

2. In *Pat Garrett And Billy The Kid*, which role was played by James Coburn?

3. In 1982, actor Vic Morrow and two child actors were killed by a crashing helicopter during the filming of which movie?

4. Which 1955 movie, starring Audie Murphy, is an account of Murphy's own experiences during World War II?

5. In which 1987 movie is a New York neighborhood saved from a nasty property developer by a group of miniature flying saucer-like 'fix-its'?

6. *I Could Have Danced All Night* and *On The Street Where You LIve* are songs from which musical movie?

7. Which famous Disney animated movie is based on a children's book by Austrian writer Felix Salten?

8. In which 1997 movie does Jack Nicholson portray Melvin Udall, a misanthropic novelist?

9 In which movie are Wesley Snipes' and Sylvester Stallone's characters cryogenically preserved in 1996 and reactivated in 2032?

10 Which classic movie featured a dog called Toto?

11 Who provides the voice of Baby Mikey in *Look Who's Talking*?

12 Which William Shakespeare play has been made into movies nine times; the latest, in a modern setting, starring Ethan Hawke, in 2000?

13 Which actor, referring to his upcoming role in a movie based on a classic play, said "I'm playing Shakespeare, and I might not win"?

14 Which 1986 movie tells of the finding of a severed human ear by college student Jeffrey Beaumont (Kyle McLachlan), who then decides to investigate?

15 Maggie Smith played a Mother Superior in which comedy movie of 1992?

16 Which multi-Oscar-winning 1981 movie was produced by, part-written by, directed by and starred Warren Beatty?

QUIZ 60

1. Who – the wife of a famous actor – played the part of Sarah Beckett in *Philadelphia* (1993)?

2. Greta Garbo starred as Nina Ivanovna Yakushova in which comedy movie of 1939?

3. Which 1988 comedy-horror movie, starring Michael Keaton in the title role, had a sequel TV series in 1989-91?

4. Who played the female lead, opposite Marlon Brando, in the 1954 movie *On The Waterfront*?

5. Which daydreaming character from a James Thurber novel was played by Danny Kaye in a 1947 movie?

6. In which Disney animated movie would you see the nasty Cruella De Vil?

7. Which Scott Joplin composition was made famous in 1973 when it was used as the theme in *The Sting*?

8. Who played the part of Rose DeWitt Bukater in *Titanic* of 1997?

9 In *The Talented Mr Ripley*, to which country does Ripley travel on his assignment to persuade Dickie to return to America?

10 Which Mel Gibson movie is a fictionalized biopic of the Scottish patriot William Wallace?

11 Arnold Schwarzenegger's first starring role was in which movie?

12 Who played the part of Mia Farrow's husband in *Rosemary's Baby*?

13 Which series of horror movies features the murderous character Michael Myers?

14 Which star of TV's *Dallas* appeared in the 1998 movie *Primary Colors*?

15 In the *Mission Impossible* movie series, what is the name of the agent played by Tom Cruise?

16 *The Moon's A Balloon* and *Bring On The Empty Horses* were the autobiographies of which actor?

QUIZ 61

1. Which Christopher Morley novel's title gave its name to a 1940 movie starring Ginger Rogers, and then to a type of dress worn by Rogers in the movie?

2. What was the title of the 1985 sequel to *The Wizard Of Oz*?

3. Who played the female lead in the *Grease* sequel, *Grease 2*?

4. Who plays the part of Sophie's lover, Nathan, in the 1982 movie, *Sophie's Choice*?

5. Which actress both appeared, and spoke the narration, in *The First Wives Club*?

6. Which actor portrayed William Shakespeare in *Shakespeare In Love*?

7. Which controversial 1988 Martin Scorsese movie starred Willem Dafoe in a portrayal of Jesus Christ?

8. Which werewolf-themed movie of 1994 starred Jack Nicholson and Michelle Pfeiffer?

9 In which movies does Robert De Niro play the part of Sam 'Ace' Rothstein, the man in charge at the 'Tangiers Casino' in Las Vegas?

10 *What's Love Got To Do With It?,* a 1993 biopic on the life of Tina Turner, starred which actress in the part of Tina?

11 What was the name of the spacecraft flown by Han Solo in the *Star Wars* movies?

12 Which 1947 movie, starring Maureen O'Hara, is about a Santa Claus at Macy's department store?

13 Which 1946 movie, starring Humphrey Bogart as detective Philip Marlowe, was remade in 1978, starring Robert Mitchum?

14 Who composed the music score for *Star Wars* and for the *Indiana Jones* series?

15 In which 1996 movie is Demi Moore threatened by a mafia enforcer known as 'The Teacher'?

16 Who received a Best Actor Oscar for his portrayal of suicidal alcoholic Ben Sanderson, in *Leaving Las Vegas*?

QUIZ 62

1. What was the subtitle of *Star Wars Episode I*?

2. Costing $200 million to produce, what was the 20th century's most expensive movie?

3. Helen Slater played which superhero in a 1984 movie, starring Faye Dunaway as the villainess, Selena?

4. Godzilla, the monster featured in a 1998 American movie by Roland Emmerich, was originally a product of the movie industry of which country?

5. The 1992 movie *The Lawnmower Man* was very loosely based on a novel by which author?

6. Which rap singer appeared in the 1999 movie *Three Kings*?

7. *Three Kings* is set in which 20th century war?

8. Richard Burton and Elizabeth Taylor played a warring husband and wife in which 1967 movie adaptation of a Shakespeare play?

9 Which number is the title of a 1995 crime thriller, starring Morgan Freeman and Brad Pitt?

10 Which Michael Moore-directed movie received the Best Documentary Oscar in 2002?

11 The planet Mars is seen as the future abode for mankind in which science-fiction movie of 2000, starring Val Kilmer?

12 Who are the two leading female stars of the 2002 musical movie *Chicago*?

13 Which Coen brothers' movie features the character Marge Gunderson, a pregnant policewoman?

14 The poster for which 1992 movie, noted for its satirical view of the movie industry, depicts a hangman's noose made from camera film?

15 In *A Bug's Life*, which insects are the oppressors to the docile ant population?

16 The St Valentine's Day Massacre is witnessed by Tony Curtis and Jack Lemmon in which 1959 movie?

QUIZ 63

1 Which actor, who played Bret Maverick in the 1950s/60s TV series *Maverick*, appeared in the 1994 movie of the same name?

2 Which actor starred with Jodie Foster in *Nell*, a drama movie of 1994?

3 Which 1992 Woody Allen movie was filmed in black and white?

4 *The Sunshine Boys*, a 1975 movie based on the Broadway play of the same name, starred which comedian – his first movie in nearly forty years?

5 Burt Reynolds and Dolly Parton starred in which comedy movie of 1982?

6 Who played the role of Tinker Bell in the movie *Hook*?

7 Which 1997 movie earned Ben Affleck and Matt Damon an Oscar for writing the screenplay? Damon starred in the title role.

8 Which famous avant-garde artist produced the 1972 movie *Heat*?

9 Which 1979 movie (remade in 2005) concerns the paranormal experiences of the Lutz family at 112 Ocean Avenue?

10 *Fort Apache, She Wore A Yellow Ribbon* and *Rio Grande* all feature which movie star in the lead role?

11 Who directed all three movies in Question 10?

12 *Mr and Mrs Bridge*, a 1990 movie based on the novels of Evan S Connell, starred which real-life couple in the title roles?

13 Which couple met on the set of the movie *Two Much* (1995) and married in 1996?

14 Geena Davis and Hugh Laurie star as the parents of which animated character (voiced by Michael J Fox), in a 1999 movie?

15 Which 1998 movie, based on a long-running TV series, tells us to 'Fight The Future' in its subtitle?

16 Which actress is *Married To The Mob* in the 1988 comedy movie?

QUIZ 64

1. Which 1967 World War II movie's plot involves twelve American convicts who are sent on a suicide mission to German-occupied France?

2. Who plays the spaced out 'hippie' tank-commander, 'Oddball', in the 1970 movie, *Kelly's Heroes*?

3. Which Italian composer has written scores for many movies, including *The Good, The Bad And The Ugly* and *The Untouchables*?

4. Which Italian composer's famous scores include the 'love themes' from Zeffirelli's *Romeo And Juliet* and *The Godfather*?

5. The storyline of which movie tells of the childhood of Frank McCourt, his enforced return to Ireland and his dream of returning to America?

6. What kinds of animals make *The Incredible Journey*, the Disney movies of 1963 and 1993?

7. Also featuring Whoopi Goldberg and Ray Liotta, *Corrina, Corrina* of 1994, was the last movie for which actor?

8. What breed of dog is Buddy, the basketball-playing dog in *Air Bud*?

9 Which actor played the lead role in the 1953 war movie *Stalag 17*, for which he received a Best Actor Oscar?

10 Which actor's movie career began with a small part in *National Lampoon's Animal House* in 1978? In 2007 he starred in *Death Sentence*.

11 The famous marching song, *Seventy-six Trombones,* comes from which 1962 musical movie?

12 In which 1995 movie does John Travolta play the part of Chili Palmer?

13 Which 1967 western features John Wayne, Robert Mitchum and James Caan?

14 Which notable composer's achievements include the score to *The Great Gatsby*, for which he won an Oscar in 1974? He also wrote the famous song, *Till There Was You,* and the instrumental, *Route 66*.

15 Which hero was played by Jackie Coogan in 1931, Mickey Rooney in 1939, Eddie Hodges in 1960, Jeff East in 1974 and Elijah Wood in 1993?

16 Who were the two stars of the 1938 movie *Jezebel*?

QUIZ 65

1 Starring Jeff Bridges, which 1984 movie tells of an alien who visits Earth as a result of a message sent into outer space aboard a Voyager probe?

2 The song *Thanks For The Memory* first appeared in the movie *The Big Broadcast Of 1938*. Whose signature song did it become?

3 Played by Al Pacino, blind Lt Colonel Frank Slade is the principal character of which 1992 movie?

4 Who or what is 'Amistad' in the 1997 Steven Spielberg movie of that name?

5 Which movie is a compilation of MGM highlight movie clips, released in 1974, the 50th year of the company?

6 What was Ben Hur's first name?

7 How many Oscars did the 1959 movie *Ben Hur* win, an all-time greatest number at that time?

8 The movie *A Cry In The Dark*, starring Meryl Streep, is based on a true story about a family on a camping holiday, whose baby daughter is taken by a wild dog. In which country does this take place?

9 *The Body*, a novel by Stephen King, was the inspiration for which 1986 movie starring Wil Wheaton and River Phoenix?

10 *Colors Of The Wind*, sung by Vanessa Williams, was the Oscar-winning theme song from which animated movie?

11 Robert Mitchum, Gregory Peck and Martin Balsam all appeared in which movie of 1962 and also in the 1991 remake?

12 Starring Sissy Spacek, *Coal Miner's Daughter* is a 1980 biopic about which country-music singer?

13 Which actor produced and starred in the movie *City Slickers*?

14 Who played Juror No 8 in the classic 1957 courtroom drama movie, *12 Angry Men*?

15 The famous scenes of Cary Grant being strafed by a plane masquerading as a crop-duster, occur in which Hitchcock movie?

16 Which movie, based on a classic American novel, starred Alan Ladd and Betty Field in 1949 and Robert Redford and Mia Farrow in 1974?

QUIZ 66

1. Which series of horror movies features the character known as 'Pinhead'?

2. Which 1973 movie, staring Martin Sheen and Sissy Spacek, is based on the real-life 1950s killing spree of Charles Starkweather and Caril Ann Fugate?

3. Who played the subject of Dudley Moore's obsession in the 1979 movie *10*?

4. While attempting to salvage a submarine, divers on a drilling platform encounter aliens. This is the basic story in which science fiction action movie of 1989?

5. *The Rock,* a 1996 movie starring Sean Connery, has its setting on which Californian island?

6. Which 1960s pop band starred in the movie *Head*?

7. The *Thin Man* movies of the 1930s and 40s were based on the novel of the same name by which author?

8. What is the subtitle of the 2003 adventure movie *Master And Commander*?

9 Which actor has the middle names Columcille Gerard?

10 A girly reunion in Shelby, Indiana, where childhoods are remembered, is the setting for which 1995 movie featuring Melanie Griffith and Demi Moore?

11 Which British-born actor played the ape, Cornelius, in the *Planet Of The Apes* movies of the 1960s/70s?

12 Which Paul Verhoeven-directed 1995 science fiction movie's plot centres on a 23rd century interplanetary war?

13 Alice Cooper's first album, *Welcome To My Nightmare,* contains spoken contributions by which famous horror-movie actor?

14 Helena Bonham-Carter plays Amanda Weinrib, Woody Allen's 'wife', in which 1995 comedy movie?

15 In which movie does Dustin Hoffman cross-dress in order to get a part in a soap-opera?

16 Who played the female lead role in the 1995 movie *The American President*?

QUIZ 67

1. In which movie does a hairdresser – played by Patricia Arquette – begin to display classic crucifixion wounds?

2. In which movie does Keanu Reeves' character join a law firm that has satanic connections?

3. Which singer/songwriter/actor appeared as Sheriff Carl Tippett in the movie *The Opposite Of Sex*?

4. Which Cold War-themed movie was first made in 1962, starring Frank Sinatra, and remade in 2004, starring Denzel Washington?

5. William Shatner made an early movie appearance as an aide to Chief Judge Dan Haywood – played by Spencer Tracy – in which movie, based on true events that took place during the mid-to-late 1940s?

6. *It Don't Worry Me* is the theme song that recurs throughout which 1975 movie that features early appearances by Jeff Goldblum and Shelley Duvall?

7. Which Gulf War (1991)-themed movie starred Denzel Washington and Meg Ryan?

8. Which British-born veteran actor played Professor Gus Nikolais in *Lorenzo's Oil*?

9 In which 1999 movie do three students enter the woods to make a documentary movie, never to be seen again; only their video equipment and movie footage are found?

10 Which 1978 movie, telling of a returning Vietnam War veteran's problems getting back into civilian life, won Oscars for Jane Fonda and Jon Voight?

11 In the movie, *Speed,* the Los Angeles bus on which a bomb has been placed must constantly travel above what speed, to prevent the bomb exploding?

12 Which actress received her first Oscar for her lead role in the 1962 movie *The Miracle Worker*?

13 Which European city is under threat from terrorists armed with a nuclear bomb in *Superman II*?

14 Who starred in the 1971 post-apocalypse movie *The Omega Man*?

15 In the 1937 movie *One Hundred Men And A Girl*, the girl is Deanna Durbin; who are the 'hundred men'?

16 Which 1978 black comedy, starring Burt Reynolds, is about a man who decides to commit suicide in despair at being given only six months to live?

QUIZ 1 Answers

1 *Gone With The Wind.*

2 Morgan Freeman.

3 Horst Buchholz and Robert Vaughn.

4 Trigger.

5 *The African Queen.*

6 *Pirates Of The Caribbean.*

7 *The Road To Perdition.*

8 Christian Bale.

9 A priceless jewel.

10 *Rear Window.*

11 *LOTR 1: The Fellowship Of The Ring.*

12 Stephen Fry.

13 *The Towering Inferno.*

14 Leroy.

15 *Westworld.*

16 *One Flew Over The Cuckoo's Nest.*

QUIZ 2 Answers

1 *Castaway* ('Wilson' was a basketball).

2 Sean Connery.

3 *The Graduate.*

4 *Carousel.*

5 *Paper Moon.*

6 Oprah Winfrey.

7 *Strangers On A Train.*

8 *Singin' In The Rain.*

9 *All The President's Men.*

10 *Whatever Happened To Baby Jane*?

11 *The Sixth Sense.*

12 *GI Jane.*

13 Michael J Fox.

14 They were all made in black and white.

15 Danny Glover.

16 Grace Kelly.

QUIZ 3 Answers

1. Liam Neeson.
2. *Unforgiven.*
3. *The Blob.*
4. *Erin Brockovich.*
5. Mary Pickford.
6. Robert Shaw.
7. Sidney Poitier.
8. *Groundhog Day.*
9. He was a carpenter.
10. Denzel Washington.
11. Arnold Schwarzenegger.
12. Burt Bacharach.
13. *Planes, Trains And Automobiles.*
14. *Dune.*
15. Boris Karloff.
16. *The Misfits.*

QUIZ 4 Answers

1 *Arsenic And Old Lace.*

2 Peter Cushing.

3 Oscar Hammerstein II.

4 *The Court Jester.*

5 *Space Cowboys.*

6 Henry Fonda.

7 *Klute.*

8 Colin Farrell.

9 Rin Tin Tin.

10 Holly Hunter.

11 *Field Of Dreams.*

12 *Sudden Impact.*

13 Five (Groucho, Chico, Harpo, Zeppo, Gummo).

14 Five.

15 Catherine Tramell.

16 Mary Poppins.

QUIZ 5 Answers

1 Sophia Loren.

2 Ronald Reagan.

3 Jim Henson.

4 A helicopter.

5 Method acting.

6 Audrey Hepburn.

7 *Who Framed Roger Rabbit.*

8 *The Shootist.*

9 Meg Ryan.

10 *Pulp Fiction.*

11 Sidney Pollack.

12 Alfred Hitchcock.

13 *Entrapment.*

14 *Con Air.*

15 *Marathon Man.*

16 Burt Lancaster.

QUIZ 6 Answers

1 Rick's.

2 *Rebecca.*

3 A necktie.

4 *Moon River.*

5 Charlize Theron.

6 *Alien.*

7 *Trading Places.*

8 A dead rat.

9 *Cujo.*

10 *The Untouchables.*

11 Billie Holiday.

12 They were all born in Britain.

13 Hannibal Lecter.

14 Cher.

15 James Earl Jones.

16 *Pinocchio.*

QUIZ 7 Answers

1 Roy Scheider.

2 W C Fields.

3 Joan Crawford.

4 A Bengal tiger.

5 Charles Bronson.

6 *Three Days Of The Condor.*

7 *The Hustler.*

8 Carmel.

9 *Bright Eyes.*

10 Six (Singapore, Zanzibar, Morocco, Utopia, Rio, Bali).

11 *The Addams Family.*

12 *The Man Who Knew Too Much.*

13 *Beetlejuice.*

14 *The Beguiled.*

15 Rudolph Valentino.

16 *Annie.*

QUIZ 8 Answers

1 *Harry Potter And The Prisoner Of Azkaban.*

2 A parrot.

3 Elvis Presley.

4 *Yankee Doodle Dandy.*

5 *Dr Strangelove.*

6 Marilyn Monroe.

7 *Men In Black.*

8 *Bill And Ted's Bogus Journey.*

9 *Bonnie And Clyde.*

10 George C Scott.

11 *The Great Escape.*

12 Taxidermy.

13 Ang Lee.

14 Steven Spielberg.

15 The Cowardly Lion.

16 *A Few Good Men.*

QUIZ 9 Answers

1 *The Last Emperor.*

2 Steve Biko.

3 Mike Myers.

4 *Blazing Saddles.*

5 *One Hour Photo.*

6 *War Of The Worlds.*

7 Freddie Krueger.

8 United Artists.

9 Sweden.

10 *84 Charing Cross Road.*

11 *Funny Girl.*

12 Allen Stewart Konigsberg.

13 Radio Keith Orpheum.

14 Francois Truffaut.

15 Paris (by the Lumiere Brothers).

16 *Misery.*

QUIZ 10 Answers

1 Kevin Spacey.

2 The Statue of Liberty.

3 Julia Roberts.

4 The Marx Brothers.

5 Overlook Hotel.

6 Aristotle Onassis and Jacqueline Kennedy.

7 *Snow White And The Seven Dwarfs.*

8 Shirley MacLaine.

9 *The Shawshank Redemption.*

10 Euphegenia.

11 A young leopard.

12 *The Seven Year Itch.*

13 Gary Oldman.

14 *Thelma And Louise.*

15 *Eyes Wide Shut.*

16 *Rain Man.*

QUIZ 11 Answers

1 *Quiz Show.*

2 Leonard Nimoy.

3 *The Accused.*

4 Stands with a Fist.

5 *Now Voyager.*

6 *Empire Of The Sun.*

7 *Brubaker.*

8 *The Hand That Rocks The Cradle.*

9 Billy the Kid.

10 *Dressed To Kill.*

11 Elmer Fudd.

12 *The Searchers.*

13 Bing Crosby.

14 *Anchors Aweigh.*

15 Gerard Depardieu.

16 Bo Derek.

QUIZ 12 Answers

1 Kim Basinger.

2 The Tin Man in *The Wizard Of Oz.*

3 *When Harry Met Sally.*

4 *A Fistful Of Dollars.*

5 Sam, the piano player.

6 *The Incredible Shrinking Man.*

7 CinemaScope.

8 He was dead.

9 Ray Harryhausen.

10 Richard Harris.

11 *Being There.*

12 *Lust For Life.*

13 Birds (movie: *The Birds,* Melanie Griffith's mother: Tippi Hedren).

14 *Grand Hotel.*

15 Fred Astaire.

16 Grace Kelly.

QUIZ 13 Answers

1 Lily Tomlin.

2 *Duck Soup.*

3 *Blade Runner.*

4 *Who Framed Roger Rabbit?*

5 *48 Hours.*

6 She first named the statuette, saying that it "looks just like my Uncle Oscar".

7 *An Officer And A Gentleman.*

8 Jones.

9 *Borat: Cultural Learnings Of America For Make Benefit Glorious Nation Of Kazakhstan.*

10 *The Fly* (1986).

11 *Magic.*

12 Gomez and Morticia.

13 *Rear Window.*

14 *Sunset Boulevard.*

15 *The Little Shop Of Horrors.*

16 Robert Zemeckis.

QUIZ 14 Answers

1 *Working Girl.*

2 *Sophie's Choice.*

3 *Last Action Hero.*

4 *Born On The Fourth Of July.*

5 *The Producers.*

6 *To Die For.*

7 John Schlesinger.

8 Anne Archer.

9 Ace Ventura.

10 *Bruce Almighty.*

11 *Flightplan.*

12 *Serenity.*

13 Keith Richards of The Rolling Stones.

14 *The Boston Strangler.*

15 *King Ralph.*

16 Marion Crane.

QUIZ 15 Answers

1 *Ghost.*

2 Rasputin.

3 Carrie Fisher.

4 *All Quiet On The Western Front.*

5 Robert Redford.

6 A dinosaur.

7 Michael.

8 Jerry Goldsmith.

9 *Mamma Mia!*

10 *Butch Cassidy And The Sundance Kid.*

11 Tony Curtis.

12 Paul Simon.

13 Christopher Reeve (who was paralyzed).

14 Mike Myers.

15 Dr Seuss.

16 *Dr Kildare.*

QUIZ 16 Answers

1 *The Little Foxes.*

2 *Apocalypse Now.*

3 … Joe Black.

4 *Phantom Of The Opera.*

5 Rambo.

6 *Earth Girls Are Easy.*

7 Leopold Stokowski.

8 *The Gold Rush.*

9 *Lolita.*

10 Miss United States.

11 Krakatoa is *west* of Java.

12 *Ben Hur.*

13 *Last Man Standing.*

14 *The Thomas Crown Affair.*

15 James Horner.

16 The Band.

QUIZ 17 Answers

1 *Doctor Zhivago.*

2 Edvard Grieg.

3 Orson Welles.

4 Tom Hanks.

5 Tom Cruise.

6 Leslie Nielsen.

7 *The Perfect Storm.*

8 *The Odd Couple.*

9 Mickey Mouse.

10 *Ghostbusters.*

11 James Dean.

12 The D-Day invasion of Europe in 1944.

13 *The Prisoner Of Zenda.*

14 Shrek.

15 A horse.

16 *Forbidden Planet.*

QUIZ 18 Answers

1. *Beau Hunks.*
2. *Cecil B Demented.*
3. Macaulay Culkin.
4. Nicole Kidman.
5. Baloo.
6. Andy.
7. *The Ride Of The Valkyries.*
8. Bridget Fonda.
9. *Cabaret.*
10. *Gone With The Wind.*
11. The Righteous Brothers.
12. Austria.
13. Leonard Bernstein.
14. Siamese cats.
15. Robin Williams.
16. Humphrey Bogart and Lauren Bacall.

QUIZ 19 Answers

1. *Goodfellas.*
2. Joe DiMaggio.
3. *Funny Girl.*
4. Barney Rubble.
5. Otto is an inflatable pilot in uniform.
6. *Saving Private Ryan.*
7. Grace Kelly.
8. *A Streetcar Named Desire.*
9. Elizabeth Taylor.
10. Michael Crichton.
11. Mickey Mouse.
12. *What's Up Doc?*
13. Lili von Shtupp.
14. Al Pacino.
15. Natalie Wood.
16. Gary Cooper.

QUIZ 20 Answers

1 Glenn Close.

2 A nun.

3 Luke Skywalker.

4 Thorn.

5 *Starsky And Hutch.*

6 *Rosemary's Baby.*

7 *Lost In Space.*

8 Janis Joplin.

9 Frank Sinatra.

10 Fritz The Cat.

11 Goldie Jean Hawn.

12 Steve McQueen.

13 World War II.

14 *Gono With The Wind.*

15 John Travolta.

16 Jack Nicholson.

QUIZ 21 Answers

1 James Caan.

2 *Airplane!*

3 Mogadishu, Somalia.

4 *The Two Towers.*

5 Elmer Bernstein.

6 Dmitri Tiomkin.

7 *The Bourne Identity.*

8 *The Maltese Falcon.*

9 Blake Edwards.

10 *South Pacific.*

11 *On The Beach.*

12 *2001: A Space Odyssey.*

13 Sam Spade.

14 Sofia Coppola.

15 Jamie Foxx.

16 Marilyn Monroe.

QUIZ 22 Answers

1 Sylvester Stallone.

2 Rita Hayworth.

3 *Grease.*

4 "Feed me".

5 *Papillon.*

6 Rick Moranis.

7 George Clooney.

8 Roman Polanski.

9 *The Lost World.*

10 *2010.*

11 *Oliver's Story.*

12 Roger Vadim.

13 Uma Thurman.

14 Katharine Hepburn.

15 Vincent Price.

16 Maryland.

QUIZ 23 Answers

1 Diandra Luker.

2 Bela Lugosi.

3 An orca (or killer whale).

4 *The Incredible Journey.*

5 William.

6 A German shepherd.

7 A volcano.

8 *Leaving Las Vegas.*

9 *Apollo 13.*

10 Elijah Wood.

11 Dudley Moore.

12 Michael Keaton.

13 Al Pacino.

14 André Previn.

15 *Moonstruck.*

16 Jessica Walter.

QUIZ 24 Answers

1 *The Deer Hunter.*

2 Madonna.

3 Richard Burton and Elizabeth Taylor.

4 Steven Spielberg.

5 Kim Basinger.

6 Roy Rogers.

7 Tatum O'Neal.

8 *Star Wars.*

9 Dick Van Dyke.

10 Zorro.

11 Marlene Dietrich.

12 *Waterworld.*

13 *Toy Story 2.*

14 Scotland.

15 A lost flight of World War II aircraft.

16 *Romeo And Juliet.*

QUIZ 25 Answers

1 *A Walk With Love And Death.*

2 *Starship Troopers.*

3 Atlantis.

4 Roy Orbison.

5 Count Dracula.

6 *Mary Reilly.*

7 Howard Hughes.

8 Michael Ondaatje.

9 *While You Were Sleeping.*

10 *Soylent Green.*

11 *Independence Day.*

12 Alfred Hitchcock.

13 Samuel L Jackson.

14 Jimmy 'Popeye' Doyle.

15 Paul Newman.

16 President Charles de Gaulle.

QUIZ 26 Answers

1 John Ford.

2 W C Fields.

3 Gregory Peck.

4 ... *Why Is He Saying Those Terrible Things About Me?*

5 Venice.

6 *Gorillas In The Mist.*

7 *Zelig.*

8 *The Big Lebowski.*

9 Pepé le Pew.

10 Yosemite Sam.

11 Joe Buck and Enrico 'Ratso' Rizzo.

12 'Spaghetti' western.

13 *Moby Dick.*

14 *2001: A Space Odyssey.*

15 Huey, Dewey and Louie.

16 Chris Pine.

QUIZ 27 Answers

1 Cyd Charisse.

2 Rodgers and Hammerstein.

3 *Postcards From The Edge.*

4 Viggo Mortensen.

5 The Saint.

6 *The Karate Kid.*

7 Tom Jones.

8 *Donnie Darko.*

9 Kevin Spacey.

10 *The Matrix.*

11 Spider Pig.

12 Wesley Snipes.

13 *Pulp Fiction.*

14 West Texas.

15 *Raiders Of The Lost Ark.*

16 *Indiana Jones And The Kingdom Of The Crystal Skull.*

QUIZ 28 Answers

1 Drew Barrymore.

2 Whoopi Goldberg.

3 Danny DeVito.

4 Will Smith.

5 *The Misfits.*

6 Hawkeye.

7 Hanoi Jane.

8 Richard Gere.

9 Nicolas Cage.

10 Penelope Cruz.

11 St Bernard.

12 *The Poseidon Adventure.*

13 *Double Jeopardy.*

14 *Sgt. Bilko.*

15 *Frankenstein.*

16 Ben Braddock in *The Graduate.*

QUIZ 29 Answers

1 Scarlett O'Hara in *Gone With The Wind.*

2 *Gandhi.*

3 Wanda.

4 Jodie Foster.

5 James Caan.

6 Bing Crosby and Fred Astaire.

7 *Rich And Famous.*

8 Disney.

9 *Once Upon A Time In America.*

10 Bolivia.

11 Rita Hayworth.

12 *Soldier Blue.*

13 *Star!*

14 Faye Dunaway.

15 *Hellboy II: The Golden Army.*

16 Joan Crawford.

QUIZ 30 Answers

1 The United States and The Soviet Union.

2 *The Man Who Knew Too Much.*

3 *Silent Running.*

4 Oliver Reed.

5 *American Graffiti.*

6 DeForest Kelley.

7 *The Apartment.*

8 The Vietnam War.

9 Susan Sarandon.

10 James Dean.

11 *Blind Date.*

12 A traveling bag and a guitar case.

13 *Cabaret.*

14 *Raise The Titanic.*

15 *Voyager.*

16 *Citizen Kane.*

QUIZ 31 Answers

1 Tom Mix.

2 DeLorean.

3 88 miles per hour.

4 Michael Caine.

5 Boeing B-17 'Flying Fortress'.

6 Madonna.

7 Charlton Heston.

8 *Of Mice And Men.*

9 *The Odessa File.*

10 *Funny Girl* and *Funny Lady.*

11 River Phoenix.

12 *Network.*

13 Rock Hudson.

14 Bridget Fonda (in *Easy Rider*).

15 Sydney Greenstreet.

16 Photographer.

QUIZ 32 Answers

1 Lon Chaney Sr.

2 Eva Marie Saint.

3 *Awakenings.*

4 Steve McQueen.

5 *The Untouchables.*

6 *Arachnophobia.*

7 *The Incredible Hulk.*

8 *Deliverance.*

9 Kurt Russell.

10 Monument Valley.

11 Gwyneth Paltrow.

12 *Autumn In New York.*

13 *Splash.*

14 China.

15 *They Died With Their Boots On.*

16 Johnny Weissmueller.

QUIZ 33 Answers

1 *Night On Earth.*

2 *Mildred Pierce.*

3 Maria Schneider.

4 Yul Brynner.

5 Madonna.

6 *Honey, I Shrunk The Kids.*

7 Orangutan.

8 P T Barnum (in *The Mighty Barnum).*

9 Carole Lombard.

10 Jeanette MacDonald.

11 *The Taking Of Pelham 123.*

12 *The Man Who Would Be King.*

13 The Thirty Years War.

14 John Wayne.

15 Sterling Hayden.

16 Kathy Bates.

QUIZ 34 Answers

1. Marlene Dietrich.
2. *Dumb And Dumber.*
3. *The Candidate.*
4. Sylvester Stallone.
5. *American Gigolo.*
6. Michael Jackson.
7. Disney.
8. Dreamworks.
9. *Fahrenheit 451.*
10. Goldie Hawn.
11. Elizabeth Taylor and Richard Burton.
12. *The Thirty-Nine Steps.*
13. Elliott Gould.
14. Bob Newhart.
15. Val Kilmer.
16. Buzz Lightyear.

QUIZ 35 Answers

1 Richard Attenborough.

2 Jimmy Durante.

3 Jessica Tandy.

4 Six.

5 *A Bridge Too Far.*

6 *The Two Towers.*

7 James Garner and Doris Day.

8 *My Heart Will Go On* sung by Celine Dion.

9 *Judgment Day.*

10 *The Shining.*

11 Gloria Swanson.

12 Pamela Anderson.

13 The First Lady.

14 Sam Peckinpah.

15 Kirstie Alley.

16 Harold Lloyd.

QUIZ 36 Answers

1 *Clear And Present Danger.*

2 2000.

3 *Sleeper.*

4 George Cukor.

5 *Lethal Weapon.*

6 The Sundance Festival.

7 Burt Lancaster.

8 Ava Gardner.

9 Gene Hackman.

10 *Army Of Darkness.*

11 The Empire State Building.

12 *They Shoot Horses, Don't They?*

13 France.

14 David Niven.

15 Wallace and Gromit.

16 Ingrid Bergman.

QUIZ 37 Answers

1 *A Star Is Born.*

2 Victor Mature.

3 Alan Ladd.

4 Errol Flynn.

5 Matthew Broderick.

6 Rob Lowe.

7 *The Color Purple.*

8 President Thomas J Whitmore.

9 Betty Hutton.

10 *House Of Wax.*

11 *Seven Samurai.*

12 David McCallum.

13 *E.T.: The Extra Terrestrial.*

14 Billy Crystal.

15 Charlton Heston.

16 Jack Palance.

QUIZ 38 Answers

1 *Galaxy Quest.*

2 *The Green Mile.*

3 Salma Hayek.

4 *The Cider House Rules.*

5 *Chocolat.*

6 *The Shipping News.*

7 Margot Kidder.

8 Gene Hackman.

9 *I Know What You Did Last Summer* (Sarah Michelle Gellar).

10 World War I.

11 *Ice Station Zebra.*

12 Clint Eastwood.

13 Howard Keel.

14 Australia.

15 Turkey.

16 Julia Roberts.

QUIZ 39 Answers

1. *Bonfire Of The Vanities.*
2. *A Kiss Before Dying.*
3. *Volcano.*
4. Ray Bolger.
5. *The Turning Point.*
6. *Lord Of The Rings: The Return Of The King.*
7. Babe Ruth.
8. *Brokeback Mountain.*
9. *Pleasantville.*
10. Stockard Channing.
11. *Spartacus.*
12. *A Boy Called Hate.*
13. *The Mask.*
14. *Natural Born Killers.*
15. *The Day After Tomorrow.*
16. Punxsutawney.

QUIZ 40 Answers

1 *Heartburn.*

2 Dennis Hopper.

3 Ronald Reagan.

4 *Around The World In Eighty Days.*

5 *Airport.*

6 *Just A Gigolo.*

7 Bruce Springsteen.

8 *RoboCop.*

9 *Medicine Man.*

10 Elvis Presley.

11 *Hook.*

12 *The China Syndrome.*

13 John Travolta.

14 *The Witches Of Eastwick.*

15 Dudley Moore.

16 *Titanic.*

QUIZ 41 Answers

1 Simba.

2 Rwanda.

3 Fay Wray.

4 Danny DeVito.

5 Mickey Rooney.

6 *You've Got Mail.*

7 Leonard Bernstein.

8 Adolf Hitler.

9 *Love Story.*

10 Judy Garland.

11 *Prizzi's Honor.*

12 "... box of chocolates".

13 Oskar.

14 Louise Fletcher.

15 Catherine the Great.

16 Chevy Chase.

QUIZ 42 Answers

1 Woody Allen and Bette Midler.

2 *One From The Heart.*

3 Diane Keaton.

4 *The Andromeda Strain.*

5 *Pretty Woman.*

6 Robert Wagner.

7 Debbie Reynolds.

8 1937.

9 Ricardo Montalban.

10 Richard Widmark.

11 Burt Lancaster and Deborah Kerr.

12 Dr Josef Mengele.

13 *Beowulf.*

14 Robin Williams.

15 Calista Flockhart.

16 Paul Michael Glaser.

QUIZ 43 Answers

1. Tommy Lee Jones.
2. Mick Jagger.
3. The Stargate.
4. It was the first 'talkie' to be filmed outdoors.
5. Buster Keaton.
6. *Atlantis: Milo's Return.*
7. Henry Winkler.
8. *Full Metal Jacket.*
9. *Kramer Vs Kramer.*
10. Tom Selleck.
11. *Poltergeist.*
12. *Exodus.*
13. *The Postman Always Rings Twice.*
14. The Marx Brothers.
15. The Dalai Lama.
16. *Tough Guys Don't Dance.*

QUIZ 44 Answers

1. *Cocoon: The Return.*
2. *The Vanishing.*
3. Kennedy, Johnson and Nixon.
4. The Flintstones.
5. Eiger (in *The Eiger Sanction*).
6. *Cheaper By The Dozen.*
7. *Hocus Pocus.*
8. *Dirty Rotten Scoundrels.*
9. Kirk Douglas and Tony Curtis.
10. *Agnes Browne.*
11. Shelley Winters.
12. Glenn Ford.
13. *Alive.*
14. *World Trade Center.*
15. *An Affair To Remember.*
16. Spencer Tracy and Katharine Hepburn.

QUIZ 45 Answers

1 *Paths Of Glory.*

2 *Excalibur.*

3 *Three Coins In The Fountain.*

4 *To Have And Have Not.*

5 Kevin Bacon.

6 *The Thing.*

7 Linda Blair.

8 *Up Close And Personal.*

9 *Finding Nemo.*

10 *Miller's Crossing.*

11 *The Singing Detective.*

12 Roman Polanski.

13 "Frankly my dear, I don't give a damn".

14 *The Manchurian Candidate.*

15 *Calamity Jane.*

16 *Paint Your Wagon.*

QUIZ 46 Answers

1. *Young Guns.*
2. Billy Bob Thornton.
3. John Wayne.
4. The Coen brothers.
5. Jay and Silent Bob.
6. *Rush Hour.*
7. *Harold And Maude.*
8. Karen Black.
9. Max von Sydow.
10. Hopalong Cassidy.
11. George and Ira Gershwin.
12. *Rope.*
13. Harvey.
14. Raymond Massey.
15. Jerry Lewis.
16. Vienna.

QUIZ 47 Answers

1 Stan Laurel.

2 Morgan Freeman.

3 *West Side Story.*

4 Lenny Bruce.

5 *Mutiny On The Bounty.*

6 *Romancing The Stone.*

7 *Armageddon.*

8 *The Joker Is Wild.*

9 *Roxanne.*

10 Saddam Hussein.

11 Liam Neeson.

12 Frank Sinatra and Marlon Brando.

13 Kate Beckinsale.

14 *Tora! Tora! Tora!*

15 Rudy Giuliani.

16 Anthony Minghella.

QUIZ 48 Answers

1 *Sleepless In Seattle.*

2 Edward G Robinson.

3 *Don Quixote* by Miguel de Cervantes.

4 *Down And Out In Beverley Hills.*

5 *The Grapes Of Wrath.*

6 *Journey To The Center Of The Earth.*

7 *Ever After: A Cinderella Story.*

8 *Kill Bill Vol 1* and *Vol 2.*

9 Maureen O'Hara.

10 Audrey Hepburn.

11 *Lady In Cement.*

12 *Gladiator.*

13 W C Fields.

14 *Wag The Dog.*

15 *White Fang.*

16 *The X-Files.*

QUIZ 49 Answers

1 *The Magnificent Ambersons.*

2 St Louis.

3 *Top Gun.*

4 The Riddler.

5 *Escape From New York.*

6 *Mission To Moscow.*

7 *Dragnet.*

8 *Peggy Sue Got Married.*

9 *The Ladykillers.*

10 *Play Misty For Me.*

11 His bicycle.

12 *Joe Versus The Volcano.*

13 *Little Big Man.*

14 Sir Hiss.

15 *Ordinary People.*

16 *Runaway Bride.*

QUIZ 50 Answers

1 Dr Evil.

2 Indiana Jones.

3 *There's Something About Mary.*

4 In-flight personnel training officer.

5 *Flashdance.*

6 *The Greatest Story Ever Told.*

7 Joel and Ethan Coen.

8 Po.

9 *Three Men And A Little Lady.*

10 Ritchie Valens.

11 *Full Metal Jacket.*

12 Kathleen Turner.

13 Kevin Costner.

14 *The Ten Commandments.*

15 *Four Rooms.*

16 Jude Law.

QUIZ 51 Answers

1 *The Four Feathers.*

2 Sissy Spacek.

3 Elijah Wood.

4 Audrey Hepburn.

5 Gimli, the Dwarf.

6 Meatloaf.

7 *A Day At The Races.*

8 *The Search For Spock.*

9 Betty Grable.

10 *Iron Man.*

11 Lloyd Bridges.

12 *A Simple Plan.*

13 3-D.

14 Al Pacino.

15 Maid Marian.

16 *Heaven And Earth.*

QUIZ 52 Answers

1 *Wildcats.*

2 Alan Arkin.

3 Seven.

4 Dennis Quaid.

5 James Caviezel.

6 A fishing trip.

7 The Kit Kat Club.

8 *Boys Town.*

9 *The Day The Earth Stood Still.*

10 A shark hunter.

11 Lena Horne.

12 Lucifer.

13 Brandon Lee.

14 *Von Ryan's Express.*

15 *Sextette.*

16 *K2.*

QUIZ 53 Answers

1 *Last Action Hero.*

2 *Antz.*

3 Boris Karloff.

4 *Lovers And Other Strangers.*

5 *Cover Girl.*

6 Doris Day and Rock Hudson.

7 Paul Newman.

8 *Requiem For A Dream.*

9 Marlene Dietrich.

10 *Sudden Death.*

11 Bernard Herrmann.

12 *Torn Curtain.*

13 Sharon Stone.

14 Brooke Shields.

15 Matt Dillon.

16 *Slaughterhouse 5.*

QUIZ 54 Answers

1 John Wayne (nickname: Duke, real first name: Marion).

2 *Chinatown.*

3 Nine.

4 *Don't Make Waves.*

5 *Gremlins.*

6 Candice Bergen.

7 Bob Fosse.

8 *Farewell, My Lovely.*

9 Will Rogers.

10 Garth Algar.

11 *Sleepy Hollow.*

12 Clarice Starling.

13 Sally Field.

14 *G.I. Jane.*

15 *Striptease.*

16 George Roy Hill.

QUIZ 55 Answers

1 Lee Van Cleef.

2 Gene Autry.

3 King Louis XIV of France.

4 *Sommersby.*

5 *Alice Doesn't Live Here Anymore.*

6 Meryl Streep.

7 *The Rage: Carrie 2.*

8 Jerry McGuire.

9 *Taxi Driver.*

10 *Reversal Of Fortune.*

11 *Marty.*

12 *Bad Girls.*

13 *The Hindenburg.*

14 *What Just Happened?*

15 Susannah York.

16 Leopold Stokowski.

QUIZ 56 Answers

1 Ty Hardin.

2 Flubber.

3 Kim Basinger.

4 Laurence Olivier.

5 Danny Kaye.

6 *Logan's Run.*

7 Brad Pitt and Angelina Jolie.

8 Robin Williams.

9 *Ship Of Fools.*

10 *Fried Green Tomatoes.*

11 *Save The Tiger.*

12 Michelle Pfeiffer.

13 Jeff and Beau Bridges.

14 *Key Largo.*

15 Katharine Hepburn.

16 Barbra Streisand.

QUIZ 57 Answers

1 Prince.

2 *55 Days At Peking.*

3 *Enemy At The Gates.*

4 Iwo Jima.

5 *The Nutty Professor.*

6 Kevin.

7 New York.

8 Eliza Doolittle.

9 *What's Eating Gilbert Grape?*

10 *Village Of The Damned* (1995).

11 Carrie Fisher.

12 Melanie Griffith.

13 John.

14 Gene Wilder.

15 Wolfgang Amadeus Mozart.

16 Gene Kelly.

QUIZ 58 Answers

1 *The Jungle Book.*

2 *Tomb Of The Dragon.*

3 *The Killers.*

4 Mike Hammer.

5 *Traffic.*

6 Charlie and Martin Sheen.

7 Stephen King.

8 Sam Peckinpah.

9 Ryan O'Neal.

10 A spaceship.

11 *Good Morning, Vietnam.*

12 Mary Steenburgen.

13 Kate Capshaw.

14 *I'll Cry Tomorrow.*

15 *The Outsiders.*

16 *Heartbreak Ridge.*

QUIZ 59 Answers

1 1962.

2 Pat Garrett.

3 *Twilight Zone: The Movie.*

4 *To Hell And Back.*

5 *Batteries Not Included.*

6 *My Fair Lady.*

7 *Bambi.*

8 *As Good As It Gets.*

9 *Demolition Man.*

10 *The Wizard Of Oz.*

11 Bruce Willis.

12 *Hamlet.*

13 Mel Gibson.

14 *Blue Velvet.*

15 *Sister Act.*

16 *Reds.*

QUIZ 60 Answers

1 Joanne Woodward.

2 *Ninotchka.*

3 *Beetlejuice.*

4 Eva Marie Saint.

5 Walter Mitty.

6 *101 Dalmations.*

7 *The Entertainer.*

8 Kate Winslet.

9 Italy.

10 *Braveheart.*

11 *Conan The Barbarian.*

12 John Cassavetes.

13 *Halloween.*

14 Larry Hagman.

15 Ethan Hunt.

16 David Niven.

QUIZ 61 Answers

1 Kitty Foyle.

2 *Return To Oz.*

3 Michelle Pfeiffer.

4 Kevin Kline.

5 Diane Keaton.

6 Joseph Fiennes.

7 *The Last Temptation Of Christ.*

8 *Wolf.*

9 *Casino.*

10 Angela Bassett.

11 *Millennium Falcon.*

12 *Miracle On 34th Street.*

13 *The Big Sleep.*

14 John Williams.

15 *The Juror.*

16 Nicolas Cage.

QUIZ 62 Answers

1 *The Phantom Menace.*

2 *Titanic.*

3 *Supergirl.*

4 Japan.

5 Stephen King.

6 Ice Cube.

7 The first Gulf War.

8 *The Taming Of The Shrew.*

9 *Seven.*

10 *Bowling For Columbine.*

11 *Red Planet.*

12 Renée Zellweger and Catherine Zeta Jones.

13 *Fargo.*

14 *The Player.*

15 Grasshoppers.

16 *Some Like It Hot.*

QUIZ 63 Answers

1 James Garner.

2 Liam Neeson.

3 *Shadows And Fog.*

4 George Burns.

5 *The Best Little Whorehouse In Texas.*

6 Julia Roberts.

7 *Good Will Hunting.*

8 Andy Warhol.

9 *The Amityville Horror.*

10 John Wayne.

11 John Ford.

12 Paul Newman and Joanne Woodward.

13 Antonio Banderas and Melanie Griffith.

14 Stuart Little.

15 *The X-Files.*

16 Michelle Pfeiffer.

QUIZ 64 Answers

1 *The Dirty Dozen.*

2 Donald Sutherland.

3 Ennio Morricone.

4 Nino Rota.

5 *Angela's Ashes.*

6 Two dogs and a cat.

7 Don Ameche.

8 Golden retriever.

9 William Holden.

10 Kevin Bacon.

11 *The Music Man.*

12 *Get Shorty.*

13 *El Dorado.*

14 Nelson Riddle.

15 Huckleberry Finn.

16 Henry Fonda and Bette Davis.

QUIZ 65 Answers

1 *Starman.*

2 Bob Hope.

3 *Scent Of A Woman.*

4 A slave ship.

5 *That's Entertainment.*

6 Judah.

7 Eleven.

8 Australia.

9 *Stand By Me.*

10 *Pocahontas.*

11 *Cape Fear.*

12 Loretta Lynn.

13 Billy Crystal.

14 Henry Fonda.

15 *North By Northwest.*

16 *The Great Gatsby.*

QUIZ 66 Answers

1. *Hellraiser.*
2. *Badlands.*
3. Bo Derek.
4. *The Abyss.*
5. *Alcatraz Island.*
6. The Monkees.
7. Dashiell Hammett.
8. *The Far Side Of The World.*
9. Mel Gibson.
10. *Now And Then.*
11. Roddy McDowall.
12. *Starship Troopers.*
13. Vincent Price.
14. *Mighty Aphrodite.*
15. *Tootsie.*
16. Annette Bening.

QUIZ 67 Answers

1 *Stigmata.*

2 *The Devil's Advocate.*

3 Lyle Lovett.

4 *The Manchurian Candidate.*

5 *Judgment At Nuremburg.*

6 *Nashville.*

7 *Courage Under Fire.*

8 Peter Ustinov.

9 *The Blair Witch Project.*

10 *Coming Home.*

11 50 miles per hour.

12 Anne Bancroft.

13 Paris.

14 Charlton Heston.

15 A symphony orchestra.

16 *The End.*